THE BEGINNER'S GUIDE TO
CONTENT
MARKETING

How to **Drive Traffic**, **Provide Value** and **Increase Revenue**

JESSICA AINSWORTH

Contents

*If you don't have time to do something right the first time,
when will you have time to do it over?*

- *John Wooden*

Acknowledgements

It takes a village… Many make the mistake of assuming they achieve great things all on their own when in fact, it takes a village to get there. And so, this is where I'd like to thank my own village.

To Bob and Sherry Cross - thank you for all of the love and support you've given to us. Our village would surely collapse without you guys!

To Steve and Jyllian - the best mentors, gurus, bosses, legal marketing EXPERTS, and so much more. Thank you all for your constant support and lessons. I absolutely love working with you all!

To any lawyers or law firms out there looking for marketing services, look no further! Steve and Jyllian, founders of Precision Legal Marketing, are proven leaders in legal marketing. Your budget and ultimately, your ROI will thank you.

Thank you to Rob, Jessica and Maxine for your support and above all, your friendship. Thank you to Patty and Alex Boyle for always offering to have at least one of the kids come over for a play-date when you know I'm under pressure! And of course, to Tony - our super awesome neighbor and friend.

A big HUGE shout out and thank you to Kat, the best book editor a girl could ask for. Also - hi, Mitchell!

Sending appreciation out to Self-Publishing School which helped me stand on my own two feet as a self-published author and to point me in the right direction. A special thanks and shout out to Lise Cartwright, my coach with SPS.

And last but not least, thank you to my family. Any writer knows that when inspiration strikes, until you get it all out on paper everything else gets ignored, especially the dishes and sometimes your spouse and kids (but especially the dishes). Thank you for the sacrifices of time you've all made to make sure that I finished this book so that I could share it with the world.

And thank you to all of you who are taking the time to read this. I am forever grateful for your support.

Download Your FREE Gifts

We've put together some resources to help you implement your Facebook Advertising strategy. From templates to worksheets and infographics, you'll find a ton of resources to help you take the next step. To access the free resources mentioned in this book (and more!), simply follow the link below:

Download your FREE resources here:

https://www.beginnersguidetomarketing.com/ contentmarketing

Check out our website for additional resources, information and upcoming books:

www.beginnersguidetomarketing.com

Introduction

What the heck is content marketing? It is a form of marketing that involves the creation of various forms of content. It is a way of building brand awareness, interest and leads for your business.

By producing relevant, value-driven content that is accessible to your audience *for free* (or for their contact information at most), you're able to set yourself up for success. If you're asking what kind of content you should be producing, the answer is this: any that's relevant to your industry. If you are a financial advisor and you're putting out content on makeup and fashion, you're attracting people who *are not likely* to convert to customers. Stay focused on your end goal of lead generation. Make sure that you are providing value and attracting those you've defined as your target audience.

Not sure who exactly your target audience is? You are in the right place. This book will help you define your target audience and walk you through a basic understanding of what content marketing is and how you maximize your efforts for a higher Return on Investment (ROI).

Creating content is not normally enough to achieve big results. When coupled with search engine optimization (SEO) and a strong marketing strategy, you can greatly increase the traffic to your website, your brand's exposure and therefore, the number of leads and ROI.

This is not a get rich quick scheme. There is no overnight success. It takes research, hard work and time. When the content on your website employs SEO strategies and the right keywords, you may start seeing results (i.e. ranking higher on the search engines) as soon as 4 to 6 months, or more likely 6 to 12 months' time. Other forms of content, such as videos, social posts and landing pages, when pushed out a wider audience, can build some great traction for your company.

It's all a process, but it is possible, and if you're willing to put in the work, you'll reap the rewards.

Image source: Precision Legal Marketing

A Note from the Author

On the heels of my Beginner's Guide to Facebook Advertising book comes our latest in the Beginner's Guide series to marketing - The Beginner's Guide to Content Marketing.

It was through writing the Facebook Advertising book that

I realized that I have the power to help those businesses left vulnerable in the wake of COVID-19. Businesses across the nation are struggling to find innovative ways to drive traffic to their website (and businesses) and ultimately, convert them to customers. After suffering a huge loss in revenue, many businesses are on the brink of closing - and many already have. This book is designed with them in mind. To be a beacon of support to guide business owners down the path to marketing success.

It takes a village….

Which is why I've put together a bunch of free resources for you, my dear readers, and all it costs is your email address (⬅ See what I've done here?!). Don't worry, we don't spam, nor do we share or sell your information.

Download your free resources to help you create an effective content marketing strategy for your business by visiting:

https://www.beginnersguidetomarketing.com/contentmarketing

Regardless of whether you download the free resources, I thank you for purchasing my book and I sincerely hope that it helps you on your path to success.

All the best!

Chapter 1: What is Content Marketing?

What is content marketing? Content marketing is exactly what it says - content used for marketing. Content marketing is a strategic approach to marketing, providing new avenues to provide *relevant and valuable* content to your current, former and potential clients. It is conducted with the intent of lead generation and building on brand awareness and brand recognition. Don't worry, we'll get to what those terms mean and why they're important in a few minutes. For those with a creative flair, content marketing can be a really fun and creative opportunity to showcase your business and expand your reach.

Content marketing includes (but is not limited to) graphics and other posts on social media, blog posts, articles, videos, webinars, infographics, podcasts, eBooks, templates, newsletters, etc. (Check out the end of the book - we've put together a list of 107 different types of content!) It is a piece of content used to not only build brand awareness and brand recognition, but also to generate leads for your business. Chances are pretty high that if you haven't created any of the aforementioned, you've definitely at least seen some of those items. If you're on social media, you've definitely been on the receiving end of some content marketing tactics. Every day, companies are paying to have their content displayed on your news feed.

Some of those may seem pretty intimidating - I'll confess, as I sit here writing this book counting every single word, I'm asking myself what the heck I've gotten myself into. If some tactics seem to be a bit intimidating, there are bound to be other areas that you can excel at. If your company can afford it, you could even consider hiring someone to create that content for you.

In addition to driving traffic to your website and snaring leads in your sales funnel, content marketing also has another key benefit - helping to establish you as a thought leader in your industry. You want to be an established and respected <u>authority</u> in your industry? Generate some content that demonstrates your knowledge and expertise. Provide value. Your information should not be overly broad but should be technical and thorough while speaking directly to your audience. When writing your content, you should not assume that your audience understands your industry at the level you do, and you may need to word things a little differently. Break down that technical talk in a way that is easy for all to understand.

The last few years, I've been writing blogs for a wide range of industries, including some very technical and very niche industries such as various legal practice areas, investing & financial sectors, human resources & compliance, and of course, marketing. What do they all have in common? A tendency to write with a higher level of understanding. Many of the law firms I've written for look for writers to come in and be the buffer; to understand the "legalese" and to translate that into something more understandable and relatable.

Going forward with this knowledge can be a great stepping off point for your content marketing strategies. Why not create some graphics or blogs that break down some of the basic concepts of your industry? If your clients were experts in your industry, chances are they wouldn't be your clients - they'd be your competition.

Let's look at how content marketing can benefit your business:

1. Increases visibility
2. Improves brand awareness and brand recognition
3. Develops lasting relationships
4. Creates brand loyalty and trust
5. Builds authority and credibility
6. Positions you as a thought leader in your industry
7. Generates traffic to your website
8. Provides value

There are those words again: brand awareness, brand recognition, lead generation... what??? We understand that some of you reading this are aware of what those terms mean, and we'd encourage you to skip ahead if that's the case. Here's a quick snapshot of the terms - this book will cover brand awareness and brand recognition a bit further on to help you gain a better understanding.

Brand awareness is important for all companies, not just those who have been in the game for a while. Building brand awareness is especially important for companies just starting out. Think of it like this: if no one knows about your company, there's not likely to be much traffic to your website or social profiles. Building brand awareness is about saying "Hey, I'm here! Come check me out!".

Brand awareness helps people build impressions about a company and/or its products or services.

When you query a search engine for something, chances are you're "Googling" it. This is a great example of brand awareness. Google is in fact a brand and not the appropriate terminology to describe what you're doing. This brand awareness associates your products or services with a particular action, more often than not subconsciously. In this case, Google is being associated with searching or querying for something.

Keep in mind that building brand awareness doesn't just happen overnight. It takes time and effort and goes beyond advertising for your product. In fact, brand awareness is about adding in the human element to your marketing.

Have you been on Twitter lately? Wendy's has been knocking them out of the park with their straight savagery and it is hilarious! The fast-food chain dominated social media by exchanging banter with followers and even going so far as to "troll" their competitors. This direct engagement with their followers and the ensuing spotlight to follow brought the company a HUGE increase in their net income. Their strategy put people back into their marketing efforts. It's not just about ramming sales pitches and pictures of tasty food (if you're in the food industry) down customers' throats until they unfollow you, it's about providing value and connecting with them.

So, now that we know what brand awareness is, what is brand recognition? While it can easily be confused with brand awareness, brand recognition is its own entity. To recap, brand awareness is about making people aware that you exist. Brand recognition is the extent to which people recognize your brand. Going back to fast food (can you tell its lunch time and I'm hungry?!), when we see or think about golden arches, our minds automatically associate it with McDonald's. And the list goes on.

All right, now that we've cleared that up let's get back into talking about the benefits of content marketing.

Benefits of Content Marketing

There are many ways to gain traction for your business. Sitting there thinking that people will flock to your shop simply because you exist is not one of them. One of the benefits of content marketing is increased visibility. Unless you're paying for advertising or to have the content curated for you, writing blog posts and designing graphics can both be done for free. Publishing them to your social profiles is also free. With millions of daily users on social media EV.ER.Y. DAY, this is your opportunity to shout from the rooftop and let people know that you exist. It's not just posting to social media either - your blog entries can help you rank for keywords in the search engine and help you be found more easily, provided they're appropriately optimized for search engines.

While the majority of your content should focus on building and promoting your brand, in order to drive engagement, you should also create content with which your followers want to interact and engage (by liking, commenting, sharing). Let's look at Star Wars Day: May the 4th be with you. Star Wars has such a huge cult following that it's easy to get swept up in it. Star Wars Day trends organically, meaning big companies aren't paying to have it pumped up. All across social channels you'll see individuals, non-profits, influencers and businesses of all shapes and sizes jumping on the content train producing intergalactic images to delight their followers.

Your marketing strategy as a whole, and your content marketing strategy in particular, should be a continuous effort to build brand awareness and brand recognition. Whether you're writing a blog, posting to social media or hosting a webinar, work to build positive and lasting impressions so that when someone thinks of the product or service, your name comes to mind. Consider this: if you've ever been injured you've likely asked for a Band-Aid. See those capital letters there? That's because Band-Aid is a brand, not the name of the actual product. The word you're looking for here is actually bandage. Be the Band-Aid of your niche.

Develop lasting relationships. Content marketing often allows direct or indirect engagement with your current, former and potential clients. Providing consistent and valuable content can help to keep your business at the forefront of their mind. Your customers won't need your services every day; they won't buy an item from your shop every day. When the time comes and they are in need of the products or services that your company offers, you want your company's name to be the first to come to mind (and not just for something negative).

Create brand loyalty and trust with your current, former and prospective clients. The world is your oyster! Offering content to your audience that is educational, provides solid advice or other useful resources *freely* (i.e. no strings attached, no sales pitch) can help your audience feel confident that you are an expert and you're not just trying to make a buck. Relationships built on trust are more likely to convert to a qualified lead and generally have a higher lifetime spend than average customers.

Use content as a way to help you build authority and credibility. Demonstrate your expertise by providing resources and educational materials to your audience. Again, keep in mind that not everything should have a price tag on it. Those outside of the financial sector may not understand what a bull and bear market is. Defining these terms in a relatable way can help your audience come to look at you as an authority on the subject, which only further boosts your credibility.

Continuing along this path, establish yourself as a thought leader in your industry. It takes time to get there, but you have to start somewhere. All you have to do is take that first step. And then another and another. Once you've established yourself as an industry thought leader, people will naturally turn to you to find the answers they're looking for.

Yet another benefit of content marketing is the fact that your content helps drive traffic to your website, pushing those potential leads further down the sales funnel and hopefully converting to a qualified lead. *Quality* inbound content to your website helps create a larger digital footprint and increases the chances of being found in the search results.

While I'm sure there are more reasons why content marketing is beneficial, I'm going to end with this last one - it provides value. More than anything, your content provides value to your audience. Bearing in mind that the larger percentage of your audience will not convert to a sale, you should still continue to provide valuable content. It can be frustrating to produce content for an audience that won't convert, but for all of those that don't, there will be those that do convert. So, keep trucking.

As many states across the nation declared shelter-in-place orders during the COVID-19 (novel coronavirus) pandemic, many businesses were forced closed after being deemed non-essential. How would these businesses pay their employees or their rent with no business? While many took some pretty damaging losses, others found innovative ways to generate income and remain relevant. Paint and wine places started offering virtual paint sessions and take-home kits to work on at your leisure. Restaurants began offering meal kits and curbside pickup.

These businesses turned to social media to spread the word by posting graphics and videos saying, "We're still open!" I can't tell you how many businesses I've seen advertising on Facebook through all of this. One of those businesses was a restaurant located several <u>hours</u> north of me. The restaurant wanted to let people know that they were still open and that they were offering free delivery within a five-mile radius. Needless to say, I'm well outside of this range. Do you know how much money they probably wasted on this ad?! I contacted the restaurant through Facebook Messenger to let them know they probably needed to refine their target audience and take a look at their geographic range. After thanking me, they admitted that they had accidentally targeted the ENTIRE United States!

It was because of them that I ended up creating a short guide on Facebook Advertising best practices and started offering it for free. Do you know how many small businesses across the nation are in peril after being forced shut? There will always be business for marketing agencies. I don't need to charge money for something that could benefit so many in a time of need.

The takeaway here is that if you're doing things right, business will come. There will be some readers who will benefit from the free value-driven content you produce but don't convert to clients. Take comfort in knowing that you're helping someone out. Just like the saying during COVID-19, we're all in it together. And the person you might help out may know someone who is looking to convert and that positive experience they had with your company could lead to a word-of-mouth referral of your products or services.

Designing graphics or making videos or even writing an SEO-formatted blog the search engine gods will approve of may seem daunting, but there are so many resources out there to set you on the right path. And if you're still stuck after reaching the end of this book, I hope you'll reach out.

When writing content for your website such as web copy (the words on each main page of your website) or creating some awesome blogs, you'll want to ensure that they're all formatted properly and optimized for SEO success. SEO is the backbone to content marketing.

If you're left wondering what SEO is, you're in the right place. In just a couple of chapters we break down the basics of SEO and teach you how to properly format your content.

Chapter 2. Defining Your Target Audience

Not everyone is your customer.

"Why do I need to define an audience?"

The answer is simple. In order to lead a successful marketing campaign, you must understand who you're marketing to. Knowing who your target audience is can help determine where the best place to market to them is – and knowing this could save you big bucks!

If you're selling a baby product, you may not be looking to market to those who don't have children. If you're selling a service geared towards those in their 20s to 30s, you don't want to waste your hard-earned money on marketing to everyone from 13 - 65+. Understanding this can save you money and help you develop a marketing strategy for success.

In mid-March of 2020, many states had issued executive orders closing non-essential businesses and ordering a shelter in place. Business owners were swept up in the whirlwind of everything wondering how their business would survive an extended closure. Without customers, how could they pay their employees who were depending on their income? Without generating revenue, would they even be able to pay their rent for their shops?

Many businesses turned to finding creative ways to stay afloat. My husband and I enjoy paint night date nights, and our favorite place creatively dreamed up cabin fever kits that included everything you'd need for a paint night at home. We were ecstatic that we could continue to have date nights - after the kids went to bed, of course. You see, we have three small children, so the big paint night chains offering virtual paint nights weren't feasible for us, as they typically began at around 5 or 6 in the evening, which is when we feed the kids dinner, bathe them and start to settle for the evening. However, recognizing an opportunity, this paint night chain had capitalized and created the cabin fever kits. I know we're not the only parents out there grateful for date night kits we could enjoy at our leisure.

It was through recognizing that at least a portion of their target audience were parents or others who were unable to enjoy the virtual sessions that they found some success.

Restaurants aren't exempt from this. Kids are out of school - in many states, until at least May. These kids have had their lives turned upside down with new school routines (IF school has continued for them), not able to play with their friends or go anywhere. Even parks have been closed down. Many restaurants have recognized this and created some really fun family meal packs. Some of our favorites are the "kits" these restaurants, particularly the pizzerias, have put together – these come with dough, sauce and all the toppings for your kids to play chef and make their own pizzas. As a parent, I absolutely LOVE this. We've even had some local bakers create some sugar cookie kits with pre-baked cookies and a couple different packs of frosting and sprinkles for you to decorate. We found this particularly exciting around Easter.

Don't worry, I'm definitely going somewhere with this and not just rattling on about some of the things we enjoyed during the quarantine. It was through innovation and recognizing a need within their target audiences that these businesses were able to at least generate some income.

Many businesses have turned to advertising on social media to let their potential customers know that they were still open and maybe to showcase some of their selections - or even to announce a new product such as the pizza or cabin fever paint kits. However, without a clear idea of target audience, it's easy for a business to target the wrong people. Let's look at another example.

One day, not long after businesses were forced close, an advertisement for a pizzeria come across my news feed on Facebook. They were offering free delivery within a certain radius and I was on board with potentially ordering from them. However, when I went to their Facebook page, I was surprised to discover that they were a little over two hours north of me. Being well outside the radius and in fact far enough away from them to tell that I'm most definitely NOT their ideal customer, I messaged their page to let them know they should consider tightening up their geographic targeting on their advertisement. After offering to assist them, they had confessed that they had been accidentally targeting the entire United States!

I have no idea how long they had been running that advertisement, but I do know that they wasted money on targeting the wrong people. You see, without a clear understanding of who you should be marketing your company to (and the tools that you're using) it's easy to fall down the trap of wasting money. As a business owner, you want to spend your hard-earned money on producing qualified leads for your sales team that eventually convert to paying customers. At the end of the day, that's what we all want.

Here's another reason why ensuring that you're producing content geared at your target audience is important. Perhaps you're paying to advertise to the wider audience just to boost engagements and build a following, but these people are not likely to convert to paying customers. Not only is this a waste of your money, but it also affects the algorithm for advertising campaigns. That last part is especially important if you're using tracking for retargeting purposes through Google Ads or the Facebook Pixel. Those unqualified leads are then captured in your spider web and you'll continue wasting your money on any retargeting efforts.

The more you understand just who your target audience is, the more you'll also understand where your ideal customers are and the kind of content that will resound better with them. People who are not in your target audience may still buy from you. In fact, you can still sell to them. Your target audience revolves around those who are *most* likely to make a purchase and therefore, are your *targeted* audience.

All right. Enough about *why* defining your target audience is important. Now, onto how you can define your target audience. As we go through this, please keep in mind that it's always a good practice to periodically check to ensure your target audience remains the same. COVID-19 presented volatile, unprecedented times that will have lasting impact. Consumer behaviors have changed drastically after the pandemic took us by storm. In 2008, the economy was rocked by the housing market and ensuing stock market crash and subsequent recession. These major events should force business owners to take a look at their target audience as it may change at a rapid pace and continue to evolve as the economy recovers.

That's right ladies and gentlemen, you can't escape economics.

So, *how* do we define our target audiences. Many business owners make the mistake of following their gut instinct and not doing the research. With a little bit of research on your audience, you'll find a higher return on investment on your marketing efforts. What should you be researching? It's tempting to come in with a group of people that you'd *like* to market to, but that's not always the right answer. Let's start by looking at your current customers. That may be easier said than done for those who have been in business for a little while. Those just starting out should take a look at their closest competitors.

Use this list as a starting point to help you determine commonalities in your current customers:

- Age
- Location
- Language
- Spending Power
- Jobs/Careers/Positions
- Interests
- Stage of Life

Not all those demographics will be relevant for your business. If you're in retail, the jobs/careers/positions may not be relevant.

Age will be relevant for most industries, if not all. For example, a divorce lawyer is not going to be targeting minors - or likely even those between 18 - 25. We're not saying that some adults between the ages of 18 - 25 aren't going to be looking for a divorce lawyer. What we're saying is that the average age of those seeking divorces is typically higher and therefore, that age group should be excluded from the lawyer's target audience.

Many companies offer products or services to clients within specific geographic regions. Even for those whose clients come from all over the U.S., you likely have higher concentrations of clients in particular areas.

Have you ever heard some people say "You know what the word assume means, right? It means to make an A$$ out of U and ME." Well, language is an area that many (including myself at one point) have a common misconception: that if you're in the U.S., your audience speaks English. We are a melting pot of diversity. Assuming that your target audience solely speaks English is wrong. This is why research is so important.

Spending power and ultimately income are areas that some businesses will need to take into account. A customer with a lower income level may not have as large of a disposable income. It doesn't mean that customers in this category should be excluded from your target audience if they are your most likely customer. Again, we come back to relevancy for some businesses. For industries such as wealth management and real estate, spending power and income levels will be more relevant.

Jobs/Careers/Positions is another demographic that may not be as relevant for every business. However, for those targeting a B2B market or again, industries such as the financial sector who may be targeting wealthy entrepreneurs, this demographic can be key.

What do your customers like to do (aside from enjoy your products and services)? What other businesses do they frequent or follow on social media? We're not telling you to go out there and stalk your clients, but knowing their interests and pastimes can help you further define where you should be marketing to your target audience as well as what kind of content may resonate better with them.

Finally, we come to the stage of life demographic. Are your customers likely to be college students? New parents (remember those paint night and pizza kits)? Getting ready to retire? Already retired?

Yet another useful way to help determine your target audience is by reviewing your social media business pages. They all offer an "insights" tab that show you the numbers and analytics behind your page. How active is your page? Have you acquired any new followers? Who is interacting and engaging with your page? Knowing this information can help you fill in the knowledge gaps to further refine your audience.

Now, we briefly mentioned a little earlier that conducting a competitor analysis can help you identify your potential clients as well. Using those same guidelines we talked about above, have a look at who your competitors are targeting and who their current clients are. Innovation can help set you apart, but knowing what's already working and what's *not* can provide some much-needed information to get you started. The caveat here is that you won't be able to get a detailed analysis on your competitors' clients and those interacting with their social pages, but again, it's a good jumping off point.

Make a statement. While we won't go into how to write a brand positioning statement in this book, you should consider making a statement that will define your target audience. Take a look at some of your favorite brand's positioning statements. We'll look at Nike's brand positioning statement for example:

> "For serious athletes, Nike gives confidence that provides the perfect shoe for every sport."

Phil Knight and Bill Bowerman, the founders of the Nike brand, were they themselves athletes who had recognized a hole in the market. Bill Bowerman, a famous track and field coach, set out to increase running speed by decreasing the weight of the shoe.

> "A shoe must be three things: It must be light, comfortable, and it's got to go the distance." - Bill Bowerman.

They developed their brand with a target audience in mind, but their brand has since evolved into more than just producing shoes for runners. What did you notice about their positioning statement? They've identified their target audience as being serious athletes.

Some final advice on establishing your target audience (and connecting it with content marketing) is this: Be willing to make mistakes. Nothing is ever really cut and dry. You're going to make mistakes; we all make mistakes - even this author. Don't get hung up on one particular idea. If something is working, remain flexible and open minded until you find what resonates with your target audience.

You always have the option to do some A/B split testing

to determine what wording or which images may invoke a stronger response from your target audience, but it all starts with defining exactly who you're targeting.

Feel free to use the worksheet we put together to help you stay organized while you're doing your research. Download your free worksheet (and other free resources) at:

https://www.beginnersguidetomarketing.com/contentmarketing

Chapter 3. The Psychology Behind Content Marketing

Understanding who you're marketing to can help you identify *how* to market to them. You need to put yourself in the shoes of your target audience and think about what would resonate best with you. What *tone* should your content have? What emotions are you trying to elicit and why? What colors will send the right message to them?

Understanding the answer to these questions can help give your content marketing strategy a boost.

Tone in Content Marketing

The tone of your content is *how* your content is written. This should illustrate how you feel about the subject being written, guiding your target audiences' emotions, helping them understand how they should feel. Do you want them to be inspired? Informed? Entertained? Knowing what resonates best with your target audience can help you determine the appropriate tone. For instance, will you inject some humor to break up the monotony of a topic that would normally be less than intriguing? Perhaps you'd like to inspire and motivate by injecting some inspirational quotes or examples of people/companies who have benefited from the topic.

Some examples of tone include:

- Joyful
- Inspirational
- Humorous

- Informational
- Formal/Technical
- Sad
- Optimistic
- Etc.

The tone you decide to embody in your company's content can help showcase your brand's personality and values.

The Value of Emotion

What does your content mean to your audience? How do you get them to read your content, let alone convert to a customer? You need to offer them a connection. Emotional marketing tells your story in a way that helps your audience connect and relate with your content in a personal way. Many studies have been conducted demonstrating that consumers will more often make a purchase based on emotions over logic. Logic comes more into play when we try to justify the amount of money we either have or are about to spend.

How well does your content provide an emotional connection to your audience?

Emotional marketing is when businesses design their messaging to evoke feelings that will cause a target audience to take notice, remember, share and buy from the company.

Think about how many times a day you see an advertisement online – you check out Google – and see advertisements all over. You visit your favorite online retailer to see if they have any deals on – advertisements. Scroll through your social accounts – you just can't escape advertisements, and neither can anyone else. In a sea of advertisements, you want yours to stand out and be memorable.

Let's compare some examples.

Company A is featuring a baby blanket. The advertisement includes just the brand name, the product and the name of the product.

Company B is also featuring a baby blanket. Their advertisement has a cute little baby running around with a baby blanket before falling asleep with the very same snuggly blanket they refused to put down all day.

Which advertisement elicits the most emotion from you? Is it the plain Jane? Or is it one that maybe makes you think about your own children or other loved ones? And how long did it take you to decide that? You have only a couple of seconds to make a good first impression and captivate your audience.

I'm thinking back on my own impulsive buy: a nail kit that I stumbled across through a Facebook advertisement. I got caught in their pixel, guys! I was stuck inside during the quarantine; salons were barely open and as I was working long hours, I started to feel like I was letting myself go a bit. There were a few days in there that I'm not even sure that I brushed my hair, let alone changed out of pajamas. So, when that ad came across my timeline, I began *feeling* like maybe I could use some self care. The idea took hold: I liked the idea of salon-quality nails at home. (I have no regrets, by the way!) You see, the company realized there was an increased demand for their product – salon-quality nails at home for an affordable price – and they set out to create advertisements that would bring in the business.

In the wake of COVID, you can bet I'm not the only one excited about the nail kit!

I don't even want to tell you about how many advertisements my husband has fallen into. Believe it or not, he's the shopper out of the two of us. I don't think I even want to know the number of purchases he's made since the onset of COVID - and no, we're by no means wealthy.

Think back to some of your own purchases and the emotions those advertisements may have invoked in you.

Let's look at how some marketing tactics employ emotional marketing into their campaigns.

Happiness

Happiness is contagious, even online. Studies have been conducted by various organizations demonstrating that good news and positive content spreads faster on social media than any other content. If you're looking for engagement and shares, this is a sure-fire way to get them.

Happiness makes us want to share.

Sadness

Empathy leads to altruism and the motivation to act on behalf of others. This emotion inspires people to act and help people or organizations. Why do you think you see so many advertisements featuring small, starving children and animals?

Sadness makes us empathize and connect with one another.

Surprise

When surprised – whether in the good or bad sense – we tend to seek comfort from things that are familiar. Surprise can also pass as fear, and brands use this to help foster brand loyalty. Think of all those ads that have shown negative consequences for using the services of Company A instead of the shiny, comfortable Company B's offering that you already know and love.

Surprise makes us cling to things that bring us comfort.

Anger

Intense emotions such as anger and passion are what helps make content on the internet go viral. Strong emotions tend to elicit strong reactions - such as sharing of posts and engagement. Some studies have found that creating content to spark one's anger or anxiety has been shown to increase virality and increase the number of views your content receives. Be wary of this tactic, as the attention you get may not be the attention you want.

Intense emotions lead to viral content and loyal followers.

Funny, inspirational or even sad pictures and videos aren't the only key to unlocking your target audience's emotions during your marketing efforts. The visual part of marketing requires taking the psychology of colors into account.

Colors and Emotions

People tend to react differently to different colors and it's never just as simple as slapping content on a graphic and expecting it to go over well.

When you think about colors in marketing, the mind tends to lean toward graphics and social posts, but it doesn't end there. It's about the color of your logo, your website, the images attached to your blogs, it is everything to do with your business.

Have you noticed a similarity in websites and logos? Blues and greens remain among the most prevalent colors in branding.

Blue has been known to instill confidence in your potential clients and trust in your brand. It creates a calming, focused and professional view and is often favored amongst the legal industry, banks, financial advisors and other corporate industries.

Yet another prevalent color amongst businesses is green. The color green promotes a sensation of peacefulness, growth and health. It is also associated with wealth. As a result, the financial sector, science, government and HR companies tend to sway towards shades of green.

As a financial advisor, you want to promote feelings of both trust and wealth, so using blues and greens may be in your best interest. The legal industry is typically viewed at with a negative light and feelings of mistrust so many tend to gravitate towards shades of blue in their branding.

Confession time... When I first started Pendragon Consulting, sure, I'd been in the game doing freelance work for a little while, but my first website was absolutely hideous - filled with bright red. My logo remains red, but my branding colors have shifted towards shades of blues and the contrasting red of my logo creates a bold statement. However, this was not always the case. Once I realized that my bounce rate was incredibly high and

I was not creating an ideal user experience, I tucked my tail between my legs and ripped it to pieces to create the website that we all know and love (because you've all checked it out and you love it, right?!) today.

Learn from my mistakes by being able to recognize when something isn't working for your brand. If you're not working towards creating an ultimate user experience, what reason do your potential clients have for hanging out on your website, sharing your content or even converting to customers?

Chapter 4. Brand Awareness v. Brand Recognition

The terms brand awareness and brand recognition are often confused with each other and some believe the two terms are interchangeable. That is simply not true. They are both completely different from one another. Ultimately, brand awareness is the result of brand recognition.

In reality, both terms (i.e. brand awareness and brand recognition) refer to two very different concepts that are interconnected directly. Understanding the difference between brand awareness and brand recognition and how to use them both to build your online or offline presence will help you earn an increased Return on Investment (ROI) and positively impact the business's bottom line.

What Is Brand Recognition

Brand recognition, as the name aptly suggests, is exactly that. It refers to your customers' or rather audience's ability to *recognize* your brand amongst others through various cues such as color, logo, symbols, slogans, shapes, language, voice, jingles etc.

If you want to understand the extent of how much brand recognition can impact your business, take a look at brands like Google, Band-Aid and Q-Tips etc.

All of these brands are not just brands anymore. In fact, the products they sell are synonymous with the name they have chosen. For example, Post-It is one of the brands owned by 3M that sells sticky notes. Today, regardless of the brand, all sticky notes are referred to as post-it notes.

What Is Brand Awareness

In conjunction with brand recall, brand recognition leads to brand awareness. It builds on how recognizable various elements of your brand identity are. Based on this, brand awareness could be defined as a way you use your brand recognition to build a connection with your customers.

The Differences

With brand recognition, the idea is that your customers should be able to recall your brand when cues related to your brand show up. For example, Apple's half-eaten apple, McDonald's golden arches, Lacoste's alligator, etc. are all examples of businesses where you would immediately recognize the brand by their logo.

When it comes to brand awareness, it's about pulling your brand from memory when a need for the brand's offering arises. The customer is not only just able to recognize your brand, but they are also able to connect with it and understand what makes you better so they choose you over others – *they are aware of what your brand is all about and why they like it.*

Let's consider an example; if you had the need for a new phone, several brands will come to your mind. Currently, Apple and Samsung lead the market. When the need arises, brand recognition pulls up both brands' names while Apple's brand awareness impacts your decision.

For companies who have truly mastered brand recognition and brand awareness, their company name has become synonymous with the product or service they offer. For instance, if you get a scrape you may ask for a Band-Aid vice a bandage. Band-Aid is a brand name and is not the name of the product. Another frequently used example is Google. When you're querying the search engines, you don't use that terminology. Chances are you're saying that you're "Googling" something. Again, Google is a brand name and is not the name of the service.

Building Brand Awareness and Brand Recognition

When it comes to building brand recognition, you start with defining your brand. What is it that you want your businesses to be known for? How do you differentiate from others? What's your brand's narrative?

These questions will help you determine who you are. You use your brand identity and introduce it through online and/or offline distribution channels. You can obtain local buy-in by approaching local vendors, affiliates and franchisees.

Building brand awareness, on the other hand, requires a more meticulous marketing strategy. To build brand recall and awareness, businesses streamline their advertisements. The aim is to market your brand to an audience that has already shown an interest in your brand.

You build on what they know by creating personalized customer experiences, offering value-added services or promotions, and building a connection with the audience through social media.

Your brand's uniqueness depends on the strategic use of

the principles of brand awareness and brand recognition.

While they both stem from content marketing, here are some ideas to help you build your brand awareness. These are all things that are covered in this book, with the exception of influencers.

- Guest blog for other websites
- Create engaging and informative graphics and infographics
- Provide resources such as a guide or other lead magnet document
- Maintain business pages on social media
- Improve your SEO and keyword ranking
- Network with influencers who can promote your brand (usually for a fee)

Measuring Brand Awareness

Depending on your objectives, some metrics you can use to track brand awareness include impressions, click through rate and the amount of traffic your website gets. Again, those metrics all correlate to a specific objective. If you boost a post on social media and choose an option other than traffic, you may find that you get a couple thousand impressions (depending on your budget), but almost no traffic to your website.

Chapter 5. SEO in Content Marketing

"If you don't have time to do something right the first time, when will you have the time to do it over?" - John Wooden

SEO stands for search engine optimization. For those who are not familiar with the topic, it can be intimidating and beastly. This chapter is not going to make you an expert in all things SEO. It is simply meant to provide an overview of what SEO is and give a basic how-to for optimizing your content marketing efforts. If you're going to do something, isn't it worth doing right the first time?

John Wooden said it perfectly. When I first got my start in the marketing industry, I was a doe-eyed junior that just went for it before realizing that my methodology was wrong. If you would have seen the first website I designed for my company you would have been horrified. Here's the thing. If marketing isn't your chosen career path and you're just trying to learn new ways to keep your business running without paying an agency, you may fall into the same trap. Keep John Wooden's words in your mind as we go forward: "If you don't have time to do something right the first time, when will you have time to do it over?"

The problem a lot of us face is a lack of knowledge. Many believe that just producing content is enough - and to be fair, it's probably more than your competitor is doing. However, that is not the *right* answer. Because after all, if you're going to do something, isn't it worth doing right the first time?

First, SEO is a BIG beast and is more than just what we're going to go into with this book. It is a balancing act. It is about ensuring your website is optimized through appropriate use of Header-Tags, Alt-Text, meta descriptions, etc. If you're new to this, you may be having a WTF-moment. Let's break some of those terms down for you.

Header-Tags are essentially tags that tell the search engines how to index your website. If you're a wealth manager, you want Google and the other search engines to identify your website as that of a wealth management company. You do this through H-Tags. H1 is the title of the page and should only be used ONCE per page.

The H1 tag should only be used ONCE per page.

Yup, I repeated that. I can't tell you how many client websites I've looked at that have multiple H1 tags per page. On the one hand, I'm glad they've taken it upon themselves to jump into SEO but on the other hand, both of my feet, all your hands and feet... No. Just no. If you have let's say three H1 tags on the homepage of your website, the search engine bots that trawl your website to index you will be very confused as to what your website is all about. Not only will you rank lower, but you may even face the dreaded Google penalty.

Don't worry - we cover heading tags a bit more in depth here shortly.

Which brings up the Google Search Console, a very important, often underutilized tool. In here, you can ask Google to re-index your website. If you make any SEO updates or add content, you'll want to ask Google to re-index your website. Before we get there though, let's first make sure that your website is currently indexed.

Open up a Google search bar and type this in:

site:www.yourwebsite.com

If after typing that in and pressing enter no search results are returned, your website is not indexed with Google. What does that mean? That means that to Google you do not exist. This is the point you'd want to ask Google to index your website. We cover how to request indexing in Google Search Console a bit further on in the book.

Okay, now back to SEO. The Alt-Text is how the search engines identify images. All of the images on your website should contain a description, Alt-Text and a title. This tells both the search engines and those who view the image what they're looking at. Bonus: This description also tells screen writers about your images, so using Alt-Text makes your website more accessible for customers with vision problems.

Some other factors that are a part of the SEO factor include whether your website is mobile optimized. That's actually a HUGE one. Go through and check out your website on various mobile devices to ensure that it is optimized for users. As you get in the weeds of Google My Business (GMB), Google Analytics (GA) and social media, each of those allows you to view the insights of what kind of devices people are using to view/engage with you. And in a mobile-first environment, chances are pretty high your users are mostly on mobile devices.

The loading time of your website and the size of your images can also negatively impact your SEO.

The H-Tags, Alt-Text, loading time, image size, meta description, etc., those are all known as "on-site SEO".

On-site meaning on your website. And of course, if there's an on-site SEO, there's also an off-site SEO. In fact, there's on-site SEO, off-site SEO and local SEO. We'll look at off-site SEO next.

Backlinks, inbound links, outbound links, OH MY! This is another big portion of SEO, known as off-site SEO, that we're only going to touch the tip of the iceberg on. One of the things that the search engines want to see is other websites linking back to yours. This says that your website is credible. The more *quality* links that link back to your website, the more credibility your website is given. Notice I used the word quality? You may hear the terms white hat link building, black hat link building, link farming tossed around when you're looking at acquiring some backlinks for your website.

Black hat link building and link farming are bad. They are often penalized by Google as well. They are methods that some will turn to in an effort to boost their credibility through shady SEO practices. Here's the deal. Building your credibility (aka authority) takes time. It is not an overnight process. Anyone who promises you more than that is using black hat methods that could cause you trouble down the line.

White hat link building methods can include things such as guest blogging, press releases, directory listings, etc. It's being named on another website that will link back to your own website. If the websites linking to yours are too "spammy" or not a high enough quality, they may not do you much good.

So, what can you do to build your own authority through link building? Commit to spending a little time each week to sit down and try to get your company listed in 10 directories each week. The goal is to try to get listed on websites who have a higher domain authority (DA) of at least 30+, but the higher the better. You can check the DA of a website by using Moz's free link explorer tool. (The link to Moz's free link explorer tool can be found at the back of this book.)

Domain Authority (DA) is a term coined by a software company called Moz. It is used as a ranking system to determine how your website measures up in terms of authority. The DA is determined by things such as backlinks, inbound links, keyword ranking, and a few other bits. While you'll hear the term DA thrown around a lot, it is not created or used by the search engines. Many experts place high value in DA while others aren't as bothered. Here's my advice: This is a GREAT place for you to learn about where you can improve your own website as well as the DA of other websites, you'd like to try to get a link from. DA is not the end all be all, but for those just starting out or going out on their own without a marketing agency, it provides a set of *guidelines* and direction.

To go along with ensuring your website is optimized, you should also produce regular content such as blogs. Blogging can offer many advantages such as establishing you as a thought leader, providing relevant & value-driven content to your audience, signaling to the search engines that your website is active AND keywords. Oh, those keywords. Let's come back to keywords in a minute.

Have you ever gone to a car dealership to buy a new car? Maybe left without making the purchase? Let me tell you, they are some of the pushiest salespeople out there. They're right up there with telemarketers. The only difference is that you might actually make a sale from the car dealership whereas more often than not the telemarketers are only wasting their time. If you've given them your contact information you'll be spammed with sales calls, flyers in the mail, and emails offering you the deal of a lifetime. It is 100% sales. And it is annoying.

If your content is 100% sales, you are that annoying salesperson that people will quickly unfollow and move on from. Offering that *free*, relevant and value-driven content is a way to keep your audience informed of what's going on in the industry, establishing you as a thought leader and an expert without asking for something in return - well, not directly. At this stage we all know that content marketing is the long-haul effort of attracting new business.

Establishing yourself as a thought leader can instill confidence in your current and potential customers. It may even open a few doors to other things such as being invited to speak on a podcast, webinar, conference or convention. That in turn could help you boost your business as well.

Back to the keywords. Here's why keywords are so important. When you're looking for a product, service or maybe even some takeout food, what do you do? Turn to the search engines and type in some keywords or phrases to learn more about what you're looking for. Let's say we've just moved to the area and are in need of a new dentist. We may type into Google (or other search engines) something like "best dentist near me" or "family dentistry in Savannah, Georgia" and poof, results appear on our screens. In Google, there are two *organic* ways that a company can rank - on the map (if you have a physical location), businesses will rank based on how close they are in proximity to the person querying the search engine and on the list below that you'll have page after page of dentists in your area. How does Google determine where your company should rank in those results?

There's no quick answer to that. There are about 200 factors in the algorithm that Google uses for determining that answer. While we do not know the exact formula as Google keeps their intellectual property closely guarded, we do know that it's a balance of authority, trust and relevance. Is your website AND your blogs optimized with the right keywords? If not, you may want to do a little keyword research. We'll cover keyword research a bit more in depth here in the next chapter.

How do you conduct keyword research? There are a lot of really amazing tools out there that can help you do your research and help you track your rank for the keywords you decide to optimize your website for. Rank Ranger is an awesome tool for this. If you're working on a budget however, there are other options. Google Trends can help you discover trends in topics and provide you some direction on where to go. It can show you interest over time as well as states it may be more popular in, related queries, related topics - all for free.

There are also some other tools out there such as the Keyword Surfer plugin (check out the link in the back of the book) for Google Chrome. This is a free plugin and while it's still in development, it also provides a great starting point for broad keywords. We'll say that as of the time we wrote this, there weren't any results populating for COVID-19 related queries. However, the Surfer team was working on developing the tool further to make it a bit more competitive.

Being a free plugin and recognizing that it's great for broad topics, it's absolutely one I recommend having. It shows results every time you query something in Google Chrome. It also populates a sidebar showing related queries and some correlation charts which show who is ranking, how much traffic their website brings, and how many words the ranking page has. Talk about helping you beat the competition.

Okay. I'll confess. I absolutely love Surfer SEO and I'm actually subscribed to their monthly plan because they offer so much more than just the free plugin at an affordable rate. If you're just starting out, you probably don't have a large disposable budget and their rates are super affordable. The two other features I really love about their website is the Content Editor and the SERP Analyzer and here's why:

The content editor allows users to plug in a keyword/phrase they'd like to focus their blog on and then pulls up the competitors who are currently ranking for those keywords. It will look at how many headings, how many words, what primary keywords they're using are along with other recommended keywords you should consider using are. You can write in the editor or export the document to Google Docs and share the link to someone else who may be writing for you. All of this can help your blog rank higher.

Here's the catch. If your website is not optimized for search engines and/or does not have any authority, you still won't rank very high. You may rank still, you just may not rank page one, two or three until you optimize your website.

Once you've created a masterpiece in their content editor and have uploaded the blog to your website (and indexed your blog on the Google Search Console), you can hop back over to Surfer and utilize their SERP Analyzer tool to see how you measure up for those keywords you used to optimize your blog. The SERP Analyzer can show you where you rank amongst your competitors and audit your blog against them. The audit will show you whether you need to add more of specific keywords, remove some keywords if you've over optimized, increase your webpage loading time, add in some words or headings, and even shows you what backlinks your competitors have in common to show you where you could also try to get your website listed.

Disclaimer: If you use my affiliate link to sign up for Surfer SEO, I will receive a small commission. This is the ONLY link in this book that I would get a commission for. It is because I love this product so much that I reached out to them to request an affiliate partnership.

While I personally use and love Surfer SEO, there are a lot of other options out there waiting for you to discover. SEMrush, Moz, HubSpot, Rank Ranger are all great websites to check out to see if they meet your needs and budget. All of those are tried and true recognized industry standards out there and are worth exploring.

HubSpot offers free training and certification courses that can help you expand your knowledge on everything marketing related, including content marketing. I am HubSpot Content Marketing certified (and a few others) and am proud to have it on my resume. Did I mention it's free? All you need is time and motivation.

Moz offers some free resources as well, though you're limited to the number of searches each month without a paid subscription. This is a great place to check your DA and even conduct a little research.

The bottom line to all of this is that SEO is vital to the success of your online presence. Word of mouth will only take you so far and as more and more people become reliant on the digital landscape, you should take the time to ensure your website is optimized for this. There are a lot of great tools out there that can help you focus on your SEO plan without having to hire an expensive agency. You won't be able to totally avoid the spend, but you can cut the amount you're spending down by doing most of it yourself.

Look at it like this: If an agency is charging you $100 per blog and it's $50 per month to use a tool to help you position your blogs (notice the plural there) for success, the return on investment is there if you have the time and motivation to sit down and hammer those blogs out.

Content marketing without SEO isn't going to return as much on your investment. If you're going to do something right, isn't it worth doing right the first time? Because as John Wooden said, *"If you don't have time to do something right the first time, when will you have the time to do it over?"*

Chapter 6. What is Keyword Research?

Keyword research is both an art and a science. It is an SEO task that involves conducting research to find out what keywords and phrases people are using to query the search engines. Understanding what keywords people are using to find businesses in your industry can help you rank higher in the search engines. Keyword research provides marketers a better understanding of how low or high the demand is for specific keywords and how tough it will be to compete for those words in the *organic* search results while offering some direction to the optimization efforts.

There are two ways to rank on the search engines: organically and through paid advertising. When querying Google for a topic such as "keyword research" like in the image below, you'll notice that the very first result you'll see the word "Ad" before the URL. That means that to get that top spot on your search results, an advertiser paid Google Ads to have it displayed. Sometimes, there will be more than one "Ad" result. Those top results *after* the paid advertisements, are *organic* results. Organic means that the search engine (Google in this case) has determined that it is the closest possible match to your query. It's important to note that keywords are not enough to rank on the search engines, but without it your ranking efforts would be futile. If your results are not relevant to what people are querying, you'll not rank well.

Many individuals do not move past the first page of search results and those that do, they do not generally go past the third page. Those listed in the top results have an increased amount of traffic to their website, meaning quite a bit more organic exposure to a wider audience.

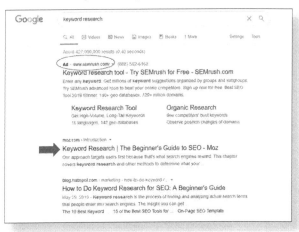

Keyword research is about validating how many searches a specific keyword has. Still, it also allows the exploration of many different ways individuals use language to search for a topic or idea. Thus, keyword researching is not just a crucial part of SEO but also a vital element of content marketing.

It can help marketers find ideas for their next article or blog post, learn about their target audience's needs, and keep up with the lingo of the always-evolving digital landscape. Ultimately, looking for keywords that people mostly use on search engines can help to create targeted content to drive the right traffic to your website and optimize the conversion rate.

The Value and Importance of Keyword Research

Although using keywords that exactly match an individual's search is no longer the most critical ranking factor, according to an SEO professional, that does not mean that keyword research is an outdated and irrelevant process.

Keyword research tells marketers what things or topics people care about and how trendy they actually are among their target audience. By researching keywords that receive a high volume of searches, marketers can identify and sort their content into topics that they want to build content on.

By researching keywords for their search volume, popularity, and general intent, marketers can tackle the questions that most people in their audience want answers to.

If you're new to keyword research and are wondering how to determine the value of your keyword; several tools can help you solve this concern and allow you to make great additions to your keyword research arsenal:

Google Keyword Planner

http://adwords.google.com/keywordplanner

Google's AdWords Keyword Planner has been one of the most common starting points for SEO keyword research. Nonetheless, Keyword Planner limits search volume data by amalgamating keywords together into huge search volume range buckets.

Google Trends

https://www.google.com/trends/

Google's keyword trend is an excellent tool for discovering seasonal keyword fluctuations. For example, "delicious thanksgiving recipes" will peak in the weeks before Thanksgiving.

Moz Keyword Explorer

https://moz.com/explorer

Moz's keyword explorer is great for finding keywords that generate a significant amount of traffic, and what makes it more unique is that it's smart! It gives you outside of the box suggestions that you probably won't find anywhere else.

These are a few of the many tools that can help you determine and achieve high-value keywords to rank on search engines.

Surfer's Keyword Surfer

Not as well-known as the others, Keyword Surfer is a Chrome extension that you can install on your Chrome browser. When querying Google, the extension shows you an approximate number of search results and how much it might *cost per click* if running an advertisement with Google Ads for those keywords. In addition to that, it also shows you some other suggested keywords and best of all, a correlation chart showing you things like how many words the article containing those keywords in the top results of the search engine have, how much traffic those pages get, and how many keywords. Take a look below:

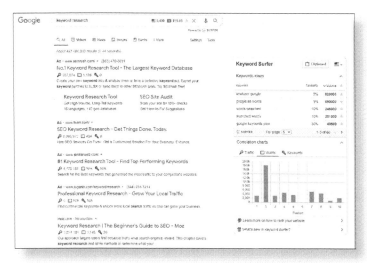

I am a believer in Surfer so much so that I've become an affiliate marketer for it. That means that if you use the link I'm providing to check out Surfer SEO I will receive a small commission for it. Regardless of the commission, I use Surfer for my own blogs to help me rank higher with the search engines and find their tool to be incredibly useful.

If you're new to keyword research and don't want to pay someone, this tool is a must. You type in the keywords you're targeting, and it tells you what keywords your blog should have, how many times each keyword should be used, how many words it should have, and more. After you've published your content (and it's been indexed by Google) you can go back into Surfer to see how your content ranks, what your competitors for the coveted top spots are doing, and best of all, tips on how to get your content to rank higher (i.e. more of X keywords, increase of word count, backlinks, etc.).

Here's the link to check it out: https://surferseo.com/?fp_ref=jessica53

The Keyword Surfer extension is not meant to be an end all, be all for keyword research, but rather to provide a quick snapshot overview - for free.

Benefits of Keyword Research for SEO and Small Businesses

People demand ease and convenience in all aspects of their lives, especially when it comes to online research. Several research shows that seventy-five percent of online users do not even scroll past the first page of search results. This makes it a challenge for businesses to get their content seen and makes it difficult to succeed in search engine optimization efforts.

Several people believe that researching keywords is just a tool for SEO, but small businesses can avail numerous benefits through this approach. New or small businesses do not generally have a considerable amount of money lying around to spend on marketing endeavors like big, well-established companies.

Therefore, using keyword research can help small businesses to rank on search engines, but it is also a very inexpensive means to achieve marketing goals. A few of the many benefits keyword research provides for small businesses and SEO are:

Audience Engagement

By developing relevant and high-quality content, businesses can ensure that their audience is engaged with the content and ultimately result in higher ranks on search engines. Audience engagement ensures that visitors keep coming back to your webpage for future reference, resulting in more views and prospects.

Quality Traffic and Conversions

Creating relevant and meaningful content will allow businesses to attract the right kind of traffic to their webpages and increase the possibility of conversions. This factor is crucial for new or small startups to attract more audience to their brands.

Saving Time

Using the correct keywords will allow businesses to save a considerable amount of time and effort. Developing content with the right keywords will not only ensure visibility but will also help to attract new customers. A lack of keyword research can make your content get lost in a sea full of other results, which is only a waste of time and effort.

How to Conduct Keyword Research

Step 1: Make a list

The first step of this process is to come up with a list of relevant and essential topics related to your business and then use those topics to come up with a few specific keywords further in the process.

The best thing you can do is to put yourself in the shoes of your target audience and think about what topics they would be interested in searching about. This is not your final topic list but rather a big dump of possible key phrases that will ultimately be cropped to a manageable group.

Step 2: Brainstorm

Brainstorming is an integral part of this process and a great way to develop brilliant ideas for keyword research. Ask yourself similar questions during this step:

- What questions do customers ask?
- How do they talk about their problems?
- What were they searching for when they bumped into you?
- Which of your services or products is most profitable?

The more questions you ask yourself, the better the final results will be.

Step 3: Turn to Forums and Boards

Almost every company has active forums and bulletin boards that folks turn to in search of conversation and information. It is amazing what marketers can find in these places. Such platforms are an excellent place to spot emerging trends and recurring themes.

Simply search for a 'key term + board' or 'key term +

forum,' and you will most likely find something related to your business. Moreover, you can head to Wikipedia, search a few key terms, and pay special attention to the table of contents of the search result to find terms you would never have considered otherwise.

If you're looking at a specific forum, board or other website you search for the specific keyword and website using this in Google "site: keyword or phrase + board/ forum/website name".

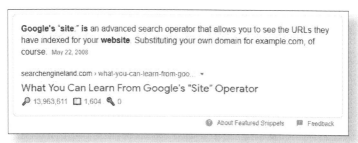

For example, let's say we're looking for something relating to the latest Facebook algorithm update by our favorite marketing guru Pendragon Consulting, LLC. Our query and results might look something like this:

Step 4: Auto-Suggest and Related Terms

The next step is to take a few of the terms to Google and enter them into the search box. Once you begin typing, you may observe that Google starts auto-suggesting terms related to what you are entering. This is a reliable signal by Google that those terms are popular terms related to what you're searching for. Use these suggestions to expand your list and go through the related searches found on the bottom of the page to get good ideas.

For example, if we were to scroll to the bottom of our query of Google for "keyword research" these terms appear at the bottom. Those are great to help you in terms of keyword research.

Searches related to keyword research

keyword research **tools**	keyword research **meaning**
keyword research **for youtube**	keyword research **tips**
google keyword research	keyword research **process**
how to do keyword research	keyword research **methodology**

Step 5: Check for Head Terms and Long-Tail Keywords

Head terms are usually shorter and more generic, and long-tail keywords are longer keyword phrases containing three or more words. The next step is to ensure that you have a mix of both long-tail terms and head terms as it will provide you a keyword strategy that is well-adjusted for short-term and long-term goals.

Those head terms are popular search terms with high

amounts of search volume. This means that the competition will be steep to rank for that keyword or phrase, both organically and paid advertising. For businesses just starting out or those that are smaller and/or working with a limited budget, targeting long-tail keywords can help you rank higher, faster without having to spend ridiculous amounts of money to get there.

Consider this. If we were to search for the term "wealth manager" we're likely to see some pretty big names in the coveted top results. If we were to convert that into a long tail keyword such as "wealth manager in Annapolis, MD" we see the competition is a bit more on par with that of a small to mid-sized business.

Indeed, there are a couple of creative approaches to achieving a top spot on the search engines and driving more traffic to your website organically, outside of targeting those harder keywords. As a business, you're providing a solution to a problem. As a wealth manager, some of the things you may do is retirement planning, create a custom financial plan, investment strategies, etc. Tailoring some of your keywords around specifically what you do versus your industry as a whole can be really valuable.

Some of those keywords may in fact be a question in itself. Have you ever queried the search engines with a specific question? You're not alone. We queried for "what is a long tail keyword" and in the image below you can see the answer to our question is found in a *featured snippet*, but also there are more results in the "people also search for". Take a look.

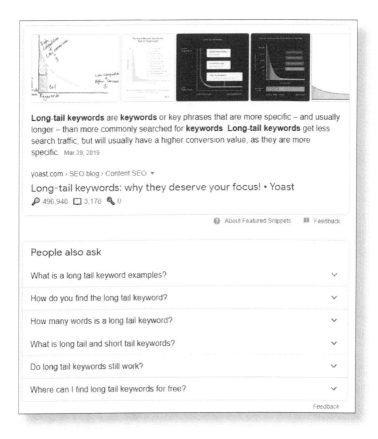

Long-tail keywords are **keywords** or key phrases that are more specific – and usually longer – than more commonly searched for **keywords**. **Long-tail keywords** get less search traffic, but will usually have a higher conversion value, as they are more specific. Mar 29, 2019

yoast.com › SEO blog › Content SEO ▾
Long-tail keywords: why they deserve your focus! • Yoast
🔍 496,948 ▢ 3,178 🔑 0

About Featured Snippets   Feedback

People also ask

What is a long tail keyword examples?   ⌄

How do you find the long tail keyword?   ⌄

How many words is a long tail keyword?   ⌄

What is long tail and short tail keywords?   ⌄

Do long tail keywords still work?   ⌄

Where can I find long tail keywords for free?   ⌄

Feedback

Step 6: See How Competitors Rank for These Terms

Just because a keyword or keyword phrase is essential to your competitor, does not mean it must be vital for you. Nevertheless, knowing which keywords your competitor is trying to rank for is an excellent way to reevaluate your list of words.

If the competitor is ranking for a particular keyword that is present on your list, it makes sense to improve your ranking for those terms and think about the avoided terms as an excellent opportunity to own market share on essential terms.

When conducting competitor research, it's important to have a clear understanding of who your competitors are. This doesn't necessarily mean the exact company names of all your competitors. For example, a big corporation isn't necessarily going to be a competitor for a small business, even if they are in the same industry. The fact is corporations have a much larger budget than a small business and are likely have access to resources that a small business may not. When determining who your direct competitors are, some things you'll want to consider is this:

- Traffic to website
- Size of business (the bigger the business, the higher the budget)
- Locale (if your business is local and not national)

There are several tools out there than can help you determine what keywords your competitor is ranking for: Moz, SEMrush and SpyFu to name a few. You're not doing anything shady by checking out the competition. In fact, your competitors are likely doing the same exact thing.

You could even work backwards if there's perhaps a keyword or phrase you're looking to rank for. Try querying the search engines for that keyword to see who ranks in the top spots for it and conduct your competitor research on those companies. If you're looking at competitors who are outside of your budget (i.e. larger companies/corporations), it's safe to say you may not see a high Return on Investment or be able to rank high for those keywords with a limited budget.

Step 7: Use Google AdWords Keyword Planner to Crop Keyword List

Once you have attained the right mix of keywords, the next step is to narrow down the list with more quantitative data. There are several tools available for this task, but Google AdWords Keyword Planner is an excellent choice for starting up. In order to get to Google's Keyword Planner, you'll need to sign up for a Google AdWords account. You do not need to pay for any advertisements to use the keyword planner.

Use any tool of your preference to highlight any words on your list with very high or low search volume. Use terms that provide you with the best balance to achieve your goals. Remember that the goal is to find keywords that you'll actually have a chance at ranking for and that your potential customers are actually using to query the search engines for. You're looking for the monthly search volume (i.e. how many people are searching for that keyword) and the metric showing how difficult it is to rank for that keyword or phrase.

Using Keywords to Rank Higher

You've got your list of keywords. Now what? Now it's time to generate some content and get those keywords on your website. You want to make sure that your main web copy (main pages and subpages such as the homepage, about, services, etc.) have the appropriate keywords interspersed throughout your content. You want to use no more than one to two keywords or phrases per page and each term should be on the page you're trying to rank for that keyword at least three times. This signals to the search engines that the keywords are important. However, be careful not to over optimize, as it could make your website show as spam to the search engines, which could downrank your website.

Another item Google and the other search engines will take into account is if the keywords appear naturally. Google is all about providing an optimal user experience. So, if you're just randomly stuffing keywords in your page for the sake of having them on there, Google isn't going to place much value on that page and may in fact penalize you for it. Obviously, that is counterintuitive to reaching your goals, so ensure your keywords fit into a sentence and paragraph naturally.

An example of *natural* keyword placement is this:

> *Dental emergencies can happen at any time, even during a pandemic. If you're experiencing a dental emergency during COVID-19, you'll want to call an <u>experienced emergency dentist</u> to be seen right away.*

Can you spot our key phrase? If you guessed "experienced emergency dentist" you'd be right. See how the wording just fits in with the content? That's what is meant by the term *natural*.

Complimenting Your Keyword Efforts

Something you'll want to keep in mind is that it can take 4 to 6 months before you really notice any improvements in rankings and that keywords alone are not enough to get you to the top spot. There are about 200 different factors that Google and its bots take into account when determining how your website and page should rank. One thing you'll want to work on in addition to your keywords is increasing your Domain Authority.

Domain Authority - a term created by Moz - predicts how well a website will rank. The score is calculated by a number of factors including backlinks and keywords to name a few. Some people take the DA score as the end all, be all. While it is a very useful tool, it is really meant to be used as a guideline, an approximation if you will. The ideal DA range varies by industry, so don't get too hung up on the score. Newer websites and those who have rebranded may find they have a low DA. This is normal. Websites that have been around for a little while, have quality links back to their website and are ranking for some keywords should be looking for a score upwards of at least 15.

Moz has a great (and free) tool that you can use to learn more about your website's DA and that of your competitors. There are actually several free tools that they offer in addition to their paid offerings. The link explorer tool is the one you'll want to use to check out DA. This will also show you your backlinks, inbound links and ranking keywords.

Keyword Planning for Success

Armed with knowledge and a list of tools, you can now go forth and conquer your content. I know it's been mentioned a few times already, but if you're really looking to boost your search engine ranking, you'll need to spend time on other aspects of SEO. And remember, it can take *at least* four to six months before you start noticing any ranking improvements.

Chapter 7. Effectively Using Heading Tags

In this chapter, we will be discussing a subtle and small SEO hack that can significantly improve the performance of your website or blog post content. We are referring to *Heading Tags (H-Tags)*.

Some people might be more acquainted with these than others, particularly those who are in the marketing industry, developers or software engineers. We are sure that many of you even use them while preparing content for your webpages, regardless of realizing their SEO value or not. However, for everyone else who is left wondering just what a Heading Tag is and why it's so important, we'll take a closer look at it as we go along.

We use heading tags in everything we publish online, including this blog post (turned book chapter) that you are reading right now. In fact, you will witness more of them as you continue down the post, so try to spot them. Follow this guide to learn about heading tags and how to use them to improve your content effectively.

What Are Heading Tags?

Before we move further, let's make sure that we are all on the same page. Up until now, we have used two heading tags in the guide:

- H1 for the main title at the top of the page (*A Simple Guide to Heading Tags and How to Use Them Effectively*)
- H2 for this subsection (*What Are Heading Tags?*)

And as we move further down the guide, there will be

several more used as well, so be on the lookout!

By definition, heading tags are HTML (hypertext markup language) tags that denote headers on a blog post or website. To make it even simpler to understand, tags are codes that inform a web browser how the website or blog content should be displayed on the page. They're particularly valuable in that they help the search engines, like Google, index your website. If your Heading Tags aren't used appropriately, the search engines may get confused and downrank your website as a result.

How to Use Heading Tags Effectively?

There are six kinds of heading tags i.e., from H1 to H6. Each tag is ranked from highest to lowest based on their significance and is distinctly illustrated by their font size.

H1 Tag

The H1 tag will normally be the title of the blog post or the web page, and although it is best practice to use one H1 tag per post, there should not be any negative SEO impact in case you decide to use them more than once. Marketers are probably cringing at that last statement. However, that information was taken directly from Google, the search engine god that they are. Please note again that using H1 only once per page is *strongly encouraged*.

Ensure that you include primary keywords that you're trying to rank for in this tag to allow search engines to understand what keywords you want the page/content to rank for.

H2 Tag

H2 tags are generally used as primary sub-headings and considered to be trivial on-page ranking factors. Therefore, we advise using them to incorporate a few synonyms of your primary keyword whenever appropriate.

This makes sense when Google analyzes a post or page heading to understand what it is about, hence including keywords in the H2 tags can allow search engines to comprehend that the content is about those keywords. Again, if the search engines can't figure out the context of the page, they won't be able to index the page appropriately and may downrank it as a result. Do not try to over-optimize your webpage with H2 tags for the sake of optimizing.

H3 to H6 Tags

The remaining tags followed by the H2 tag must be used to represent the rest of the sub-heading hierarchy within a specific page or blog post.

The most crucial thing is that each heading or sub-heading must clearly define the content section it begins and logically structures the page or post.

Here is an excellent example of a logically structured post may look like:

- H1: What is market gardening farming?
  - H2: The benefits of market gardening farming
    - H3: Higher profits
    - H3: Experimentation
    - H3: Less labor

- H2: The shortcomings of market gardening farming
  - H3: Limited produce
  - H3: Requires diligence

Pro Tip: Always structure your headings well and use primary keywords in them.

When to Use Heading Tags?

Whether you are working on a blog post or website pages, make sure to include heading tags on each page! Using them effectively will provide a hierarchical structure to your content and help readers navigate the post quickly.

It is vital to ensure that structure is not disrupted, and tags are not missed out. Failure to do so will confuse Google and make the content unstructured. Generally, H1-H4 tags are used majorly for webpages and blog posts, whereas H5 and H6 are used for very long and in-depth pieces of writing.

Why Use Headings Tags?

There are a number of reasons why your website and all of the content on it should use heading tags, including:

1. Boost SEO
2. Improve Accessibility
3. Provide Structure

Boost SEO

While Heading Tags may not directly impact your SEO, it can indirectly impact it in a number of ways when employed correctly and effectively. It creates content of a higher quality that is easier to read and a better text is favorable for users, and thus better for your SEO. The search engines prefer content that they are able to understand and classify but also, they prefer content that provides optimal user experiences.

If visitors do not easily find what they are looking for, they may leave your webpage and turn to your competition's website to answer their queries. This is why the structure and headings used in your content would impact your SEO.

Improve Accessibility

Heading structure is vital for accessibility, especially for visitors who cannot easily read via a screen. As heading tags are in HTML, a person reading from a screen can easily view and understand the article structure and content.

By listening to or reading the headings on a post, visually challenged people can decide whether they want to read more about the content or not. Moreover, screen readers provide shortcuts to jump from one heading to another to provide navigation to readers.

And let's not forget that what's good for accessibility is also favorable for SEO!

Provide Structure

Heading tags allow readers to navigate through your blog post or website effortlessly, providing an optimal user experience. Therefore, it is vital to indicate what a paragraph or section is about, or visitors (and search engine bots) would not know what to expect.

Readers generally like to quickly skim through content, to decide which section of the content they are going to read. Adding h-tags drastically helps them do that as the skimming process becomes significantly more accessible for readers when it contains headings.

Chapter 8. Understanding Inbound Links

An essential piece to the SEO puzzle is links. An effective SEO strategy employs link building methods to help drive your company up in search engine rankings. Links are generally divided into three different categories: inbound links, internal links, and outbound links. They can be defined as follows:

Inbound links: Links from another website that point to your site.

Outbound links: Links that direct you to another website.

Internal links: Links used for navigating a website or blog post by linking one page of the website to another page of the same website.

All three types of links are vital to have, but the most coveted are usually inbound links. What exactly are inbound links? And how do they benefit businesses?

What are Inbound Links?

Inlinks, inbound links or backlinks, are all the same thing. It is a simple, essential part of the internet that hyperlinks one webpage to another. Inbound is typically used by the person receiving the link and simply means links that refer back to your blog post or website.

If you've spent even a little time in the SEO industry, you'll know that SEO experts spend their entire careers specializing in gathering links. But why are they so sought-after, and how can you get them?

How Inbound Links Benefit Businesses?

In the SEO industry, usually links equal profits as they drive more traffic to your website and more traffic means more potential users to convert into customers. But why is that? Read on further to learn how inbound links benefit businesses.

Benefit #1: Generate More Traffic

One of the main benefits to inbound links is that it generates more traffic to your website. Of course, more traffic means the more chances you have of converting that traffic into paying customers. Inbound links can help drive traffic to your website through two primary means: By improving SERP ranking and through referral traffic.

Improve SERP Ranking

Inbound links improve the ranking of a business website or blogpost on the search engine result pages (SERP). The higher your website is ranking for certain keywords, the more chances you will have to increase traffic on your web page. The absence of inbound links, in fact, may lower your chances to rank on the search engines (like Google) at all. Therefore, if you want to boost traffic to your website or blog post, make sure you're using inbound links in your SEO strategy.

Referral Traffic

Referral traffic comes from inbound links that direct traffic to your website. When a directory, citation, blog post, etc. links back to your website and users are clicking on that link, they are "referred" to your website by the initial website they found your link on. Hence the term referral traffic.

The volume of traffic received by a referral link depends entirely upon the traffic received by the website or blog post in the first place. If you're looking to work on creating inbound links, you can use tools such as Moz or SEMrush to help you determine how much traffic the website in question is receiving to help determine if the link would be beneficial for you. It is crucial to ensure that you take advantage of inbound links by including information about your website/blog to the linking website. This means that you will generate traffic from your desired target audience, and this the kind of traffic that you can effectively convert into sales.

Side note: *When deciding whether a link would be valuable for you, you should also take into account a website's spam score. Google does not place much value in websites that are spammy.*

Benefit #2: High-Quality SEO Content

Since the inception of Google's Panda update, the quality of content on a website or blogpost matters considerably more. Those days are bygone when businesses could sprinkle poor quality content on their webpages with phrases and keywords just for the sake of doing it. Now is the era when people want content that has some worth to it. So, what exactly qualifies as high-quality content?

Although there may be several other factors to contend for quality content, it is fair to accept that it embraces the following criteria:

Creative – content should be interesting, useful and

attention grabbing

Relevant – the material should be relatable to your content

Unique – it should be unique and not the same tired angle that your competitors are offering

Producing a plethora of content each week is futile until and unless your content is creative, relevant, and unique. To persuade other webpages to backlink to yours, it is vital that you provide *high-quality content* and ultimately escalate the number of quality backlinks to your domain.

Benefit #3: Increase Brand Awareness

Besides boosting your company's SEO strategy, backlinks or inbound links are an excellent way to build and increase brand awareness. Search engines treat quality inbound links as a sign of approval for another source. For example, if The New York Times or other authority website, backlinks to your domain, it indicates to Google that your web page is a source of relevant, legitimate, and credible information. This ensures that you climb the SERP ladder and foster brand awareness among your target audience.

By improving inbound links, businesses can show that they have done the research to find authoritative and credible pages. Moreover, social media, along with other marketing techniques, can serve as a way of demonstrating authority within your industry or niche.

Benefit #4: Stay Ahead of Competition

Another key benefit provided by backlinks is to stay ahead

of your competitors. Building inbound links improves your standing against other major players present in your niche industry.

For instance, if you are endorsing a service or product that is very niche, getting another player of the industry to backlink to your webpage can do wonders to put you ahead of your competitors. In a way, those links serve as an endorsement of your website.

Improving inbound strategy can significantly expose your business to a broader target audience.

How to Get Inbound Links?

Now that you know the significance of inbound links, you may be wondering how to get them. So, what is the secret behind receiving a ton of high-quality inbound links?

Although there are several tips and tricks to boost the number of links directed to your website, you cannot escape the hard truth. To generate a successful link-building strategy, a significant amount of time and hard work is required. A couple of common ways to build inbound links include:

- Develop new high-quality content that is interesting, creative, informative, and link worthy.
- Try getting backlink references by publications, industry leaders, and other prominent figures.
- Get the most out of existing links. Make sure the links are operational and not broken.
- Leverage existing relationships because chances are if any publication uses your backlink, then you both might have similar audiences.

- Collaborate with industry thought leaders, organizations, networking groups, peers, etc. to further optimize your link building strategy.

These are only a few of the many ways you can get inbound links. Just ensure that you are producing quality content that aligns with your brand. If readers enjoy the content, chances are they will keep coming back for more.

Inbound links are a valuable component of SEO, therefore, try to build links that entail quality and provide genuine value to your target audience. Adding links just for the sake of it can make matters worse instead of helping your website flourish.

Chapter 9. All About Blogging

Content marketing takes many different forms, one of which is blogging. I can almost hear the collective groans (and maybe even a few swear words) as I write this. There are many advantages of blogging, but we'll get to those in a minute. When consulting with a marketing agency on SEO and/or lead generation, they may recommend blogging to you. Why? Because blogging has the power to help you rank higher and establish you as a thought leader in your industry. And that's not all.

When working with clients on their marketing strategies, some of the most common questions we get are: Why should I blog? Can a blog really help my business grow? Can it help me rank higher in search engines? The short answer is yes, it can help with all of those when done correctly. Notice we used the term *correctly*, right?

Here's the deal, search engines love websites that are continually updated with new content. Sitting down to hammer out a blog when inspiration strikes is great. In fact, it's probably more than some of your competitors are doing. However, if you're not optimizing your blogs, they may not have the desired impact. Sure, it will help to establish you as an authority regardless but following some best practices can get you much more than that. If you're working hard to produce relevant and value-driven content, isn't it worth optimizing it to reap the most reward? Keep this in mind: You may be doing more than some of your competitors by producing content, but if you're not optimizing, you're not really competing.

Do you remember our quote from the previous chapter?

If you don't have time to do something right the first time, when will you have time to do it over?

- *John Wooden*

There are those that may prefer the stance of "it's not a competition". If you'd prefer to think of it another way, think of it like this. Creating content without optimizing means you MAY be able to rank on the search engines, but it's not likely to be very high - meaning you're the 47th result to show up for a specific keyword/key phrase. That means that you're not on the first page, not even on page two or three of the search results. Let's look at some statistics:

According to HubSpot, there are 34,000 Google queries PER SECOND and over one trillion searches per month. That's a LOT of searches! Of those searches, 75 percent of users never go past the first page. What does this mean? That means that unless you're ranking on the first page for what your customers are looking for, you're not very visible. With all of that in mind, let's jump in.

In this chapter, we'll talk about:

- Ways blogging can help your business grow
- Review case studies
- 10 principles of blogging
- Determining whether your strategy is working

Benefits of Blogging

We talked about a couple of the benefits of blogging briefly already, but let's dive a bit deeper into the sea of benefits:

- Thought leadership
- Relevant, value-driven content
- Driving traffic to your website
- Keywords/Search engine ranking
- Continuously updated content

Many business owners either don't have time or don't see the value in blogging and so often, don't take advantage.

Thought Leadership

What is a thought leader?

A thought leader can be an individual or a company that is regarded by prospects, clients, associates and even competitors as a trusted source or authority within their respective industry. A thought leader offers unique advice, guidance and provides inspiration to others in their industry.

How do you become a thought leader?

If you're wondering how to become a thought leader in your industry, you're not alone. Establishing yourself as a thought leader takes time and effort. You also can't just declare yourself a thought leader - the elusive title is one that is bestowed upon you. Continue to produce relevant and value-driven content, and it will come.

There is value in the early stages as well. You may not be an influencer or even well-known within your industry, but that doesn't mean that the content you're producing is worthless. Your clients and potential clients want to know that you're an expert in your industry - or at least competent enough that they can rely on your product or services. This brings us to our next benefit.

Relevant, Value-Driven Content

It can take years to establish yourself as an expert to those in your industry. It may take less time to prove yourself to your clients. Producing relevant, value-driven content for free can help your clients and potential clients come to trust you. It can help to instill trust in those who are likely to frequent your business.

Understand your client's problem and provide the solution. Build a relationship with them built on trust for a lasting and fruitful relationship.

Driving Traffic to Your Website

By producing relevant and value-driven content, such as blogs, you're providing a reason for people to visit your website AND to spend time there. Google Analytics is a beast and is also essential. If you haven't put a Google Analytics code on your website, you're behind the curve. That is a beast for another day, and we won't go into it in this book beyond telling you to install the code and talking about the bounce rate.

Some of the information you can monitor on Google Analytics is how much traffic your website is getting, when the busiest day and time of the week are, how many visits to each page and your bounce rate. Again, there is so much more that you could do, but we're not going to go into that in this book.

The bounce rate is the rate of visitors to your website who navigate away after viewing only one page. A higher bounce rate means that people aren't staying on your website and it may be a sign that you should consider restructuring your home page. If your website has a higher bounce rate, search engines like Google won't place much value in your website and it may cause you to rank lower.

Failure is the ladder to success.

If your bounce rate is high, it may be indicative that you need to change things or add in some valuable content, but it does not mean that you should quit. Failure paves the way to success; You just need to get up and try again. When we first started our company, our website was atrocious! However, after identifying the problem we sought the solution to improve our website and the overall experience for our users. So, just keep on keeping on. We have faith in you!

All right. Enough of that and back to the learning. How can blogging help your bounce rate? Well, by providing content on your website, such as blogs, that provides engaging information that your audience would actually *want* to read, it will keep them on your website longer and decrease the bounce rate. Do we need to say that last part again??

Engaging content, such as a blog, entices users to spend more time on your website and therefore will decrease the bounce rate. That lower bounce rate will signal to the search engines that you are producing engaging content and may improve your ranking for certain keywords. This leads us to our next subtopic.

Keywords and Search Engine Ranking

When we broach the subject of keywords/key phrases, the majority of business owners we've spoken to have no idea what we're talking about. Look at keywords from this standpoint:

You are a potential customer who is looking to find a new dentist. Perhaps you've asked a friend for a referral and then looked them up online to get their contact info and check out their reviews. Maybe you've just gone straight to the search engine. Either way, at some point we end up at the search engine. What do you do now? You type in a keyword or key phrase to bring up results that are relevant to your query. For this example, let's say you typed in "family dentist in Orlando, FL". (I've got theme parks on the mind!)

Let's say there are 10,000 people searching for those exact keywords every single month. If your website doesn't have them, you are not competing for customers. You're not even in the running. Not even in the bandstands. You will most likely _not_ be found by those 10k people who are looking for a family dentist in Orlando.

This is where we tell you that you need to do your homework. You need to find out what words and phrases your potential customers are querying and place these on your website if they're not there already - and we don't mean one and done. While you should still conduct research on what people are querying, you should also check out what your competitors are doing. This can provide you a great jumping off point.

The trick is to make sure that keywords appear natural and that you aren't over optimizing your content in there. Keyword stuffing can negatively impact your search engine ranking. There are loads of tools out there that can help you accomplish your keyword research - some free, most paid.

If you need a refresher on keyword research, hop back over to that chapter.

Continuously Updated Content

<u>Bottom Line Up Front (BLUF):</u> Websites who do not continually provide fresh content will be viewed as static websites (aka dead) by the search engines, as you aren't offering up anything new.

The search engines use bots to crawl your website. The newer content your website provides, the more your website will be indexed. This does *not* mean that you will rank higher simply based on frequent indexing. It means that you'll have more *opportunities* to rank higher.

Google has over 200 factors that go into determining how well your website will rank in the search engines and it's all really a balancing act. Is your website credible? Does your content have the right blend of keywords? What is your website's authority? While you may feel like your answer to all of those is yes, what do the numbers tell you? How many keywords are you ranking for? How many quality backlinks does your website have? Are you producing relevant and engaging content to drive traffic?

Case Studies

The benefits of blogging are there, for sure, but not without a fair bit of effort. So, if you're going to make the effort, you'll probably want to know that it works before investing your time (and money if you're paying someone to do it for you) in blogging.

Steven Long, founder of Precision Legal Marketing, shared with us just how well blogging coupled with SEO worked during COVID-19.

"When COVID first hit we had a client in mid-town Manhattan literally go dark because courts were suddenly shuttered. With 8 attorneys on their staff, everyone had time to fill. So, we put them to work writing family law blog content related to COVID. We covered the gamut of what to do if your co-parent has COVID (do you still send your child to their house) to how to get along in quarantine with a spouse you know you want to divorce. Within days, we had 18-20 pieces published on the site. We have never posted new content for one client this quickly, so it was a real challenge for our team to maintain SEO integrity while essentially rushing this content. Within a week of publishing this content, we saw traffic literally double. We had national rank for COVID/divorce keywords and even out ranked major NYC news outlets and other national sites. While we don't want national traffic on the site per se, the traffic was mostly New Yorkers doing national broad keyword type searches. Google wasn't yet algorithmically caught up, so we immediately benefited. Months later, the site's traffic has stayed at those new levels, so it wasn't just a flash in the pan. The search engines were hungry for content, and we fed them."

10 Principles of Blogging

As with everything, there are some best practices, or principles, to blogging. Your heart may be in the right place with some well-meaning blogs, but when they're not optimized for users queries and the search engines, they may fall flat. And here's the best part: If you already have some blogs on your website, you can republish them as if they were new once you've updated them to be a bit more user and search engine friendly.

Let's take a look at the 10 principles of blogging.

1. **Define Your Target Audience** - Not everyone is your customer. Write to those who are likely to convert to clients. What common interests does your customer have? If you own a pet store, you know that your customers are all going to be interested in pets.

2. **Conduct Topic Research** - Seasons change, the economy goes through hardships, and every once in a while, a major event such as a pandemic occurs. Stay ahead of the curve by researching what topics are relent at that time. For instance, during COVID-19 many pet owners were concerned that their pets were either carriers or could contract the virus. Keeping your customers informed of these hot topics can drive traffic to your website and help build your brand awareness.

3. **Conduct Keyword Research** - We already talked about this one and why it's important. Have a look at what keywords you'd like your website to rank higher for and try to shape your blog around them. Going back to our pet shop example, we may want to rank higher for includes a selection of pet grooming

products. With more time being spent at home during the pandemic, pet owners were having to take grooming into their own hands. A blog on "Five Tips to Grooming Your Pet at Home" would be a topic that would elicit some interest and you could use the keywords for your grooming products in the article.

4. **Inbound and Outbound Links** - Inbound links are links in your article (or other section of your website) that link to other articles or sections of your website. Outbound links refer to links that go to other websites. As a general rule of thumb, you should have at least one or two of each in your article. Now, you're not just throwing a random URL in there, you're highlighting a word and then hyperlinking the word(s) to the inbound or outbound URL.

5. **SEO Formatting** - You can't escape SEO formatting! Just like the rest of your page, your blog or article should include a title, which will be your H1 tag (Heading Tag AKA H-Tag), and your subtitles which will be your H2, H3 and H4 tags. These tags are important, as they help the search engine determine how to index your website. If the search engines get confused, you won't rank as high even if you've met all of the other factors in their algorithm.

6. **Minimum Word Count** - It's tempting to just throw a couple of paragraphs out there, but you should aim for a minimum of about 600 words. If you can, aim higher. While 600 words would have been enough to rank in prior years, these days you really need to have about 1500+ words to be competitive. The longer content is appearing on page one of the search engines.

7. **Ensure Readability** - Write to your reader. Many businesses write as if they were writing to other professionals in the industry. What do I mean by that? Lawyers often have difficulty conveying a message that those of us without a background in law could really understand. That is often jokingly called "legalese". You've got to find a way of translating that legalese into wording that those without a background in your industry can understand. For instance, if someone is looking for a financial advisor to help create a financial plan and invest some money for retirement, they may not understand all of the terms like S&P 500, haircut (totally different meaning in financial talk!), bear market, etc. Before delving into a topic like that, you must first clarify what a haircut is in financial speak.

   When writing your blogs, you want to make sure that your readers can fully understand what you're putting out there. In addition to that, you want to put your best foot forward by ensuring your post is free of spelling and grammatical errors.

8. **Keep Your Personal Opinions to Yourself & Avoid Controversial Topics** - It's tempting to join in those hot topics surrounding controversial issues, politics, or to express your opinion. Save that for your personal (and private) lives. Unless your business' brand is built around a certain controversial issue, you run the risk of alienating a percentage of your potential clients. Even worse, participating in a controversial issue may make your business go viral for all the wrong reasons, which could lead to you being forced to close shop.

9. **Be Objective** - Dial down the sales pitch. We've all gotten called by some pushy salespeople who can't take no for an answer. Don't be that pushy salesperson. To really build your brand and a loyal following, provide your readers with relevant and valuable information minus the sales pitch. It's okay to conclude your blog with a call to action, but you shouldn't be ramming your "buy now" pitch down their throats. You may offer an awesome product or service, but eventually your pushiness will be enough to drive them away.

    Being objective also means being unbiased. Of course, you'll be biased towards your own products or services, but on the topic you are writing you, refrain from taking sides.

10. **Promote It!** - You just wrote a kick a$$ blog! Go out there and tell the world!! Share your blog on social media. Consider pushing your blogs out to Facebook, LinkedIn, Twitter, Instagram AND Google My Business. Not all of those will be relevant to all industries. Google My Business is a great way to put information out there, especially blogs, but is often underutilized for that purpose. It's free and your business should already have a GMB profile, so why not?! It's just one more way for you to drive traffic to your website.

Determining Whether Blogging is Working

Blogging is the long-haul game. There are no overnight success options and anyone who tells you otherwise is lying to you. Realistically, if your website's SEO is in good shape and you've optimized your website with the appropriate keywords and key phrases, including your blog section, you're looking at about four to six months on average to start seeing results. Don't be discouraged. Keep leveraging your keywords and producing relevant, continuous content, and your hard work will pay off.

Let's set some realistic expectations here as well. In four to six months when you start seeing results, you're most likely *not* going to be on page one. You may not even be hitting page two or three, but if you're in the top 50 you're going somewhere! When you start ranking for those keywords, keep building on them to continually improve your ranking. Remember that your competitors are still out there hustling. If you don't keep up with them or if you let your content grow stagnant, you'll lose any ground you've gained.

Here are some metrics you can use to measure some of the items we've talked about in this chapter.

To track the bounce rate (and various other metrics) on your website, you'll want to install a Google Analytics code on your website. You can download the app and track everything real-time on your phone. This tool is completely free.

Domain Authority (DA) is a ranking metric created by a software company called Moz. Moz has some really great - a couple free - tools on their website. One of those free tools is the link explorer. This tool will show you your DA and some of the factors that it took into account to give you that ranking. It will show you how your DA has changed over time, every link that links back to your website (backlinks), how many inbound links you have, how many and what keywords your website is ranking for, etc.

In addition to Moz, there are several other tools out there that you can use to track how you're ranking for keywords - most of them are paid. One of our favorites is Rank Ranger. This tool offers quite a number of capabilities, including the ability to track keyword rank AND to conduct keyword research.

While you're checking out your own link in Moz, check out your competitor's website as well to give you some idea of links you could try to get a backlink from or even keywords you should be trying to rank for.

Can you tell I have a love for writing?! All right. This was a really long chapter and we'll give you a break before diving into the next segment.

Chapter 10. Ask Google to Re-Index Your Website

If you've made any changes or updates to your website, such as to your web copy, your structure, or even adding a blog entry, you'll want to alert Google to re-index your website, or at least the new page you've just updated or added and not necessarily the whole website (unless you've just built or completely restructured/rewritten your website). Without making this request, it can take a few weeks or even months before Google's bots crawl your website to re-index it on its own.

Google has bots that crawl every page out there on the internet in order to gather information and organize it in the Search index.

Let's simplify this a bit for those not familiar with this topic. If your website is not indexed by Google/Google's bots, it will not appear in Google's search results. If you're trying to maximize your exposure or to rank for specific keywords, you can see where the problem lies.

Do you remember our chapter on heading tags? One of the things we mentioned was that for Google (and the other search engines) to understand your website and how to index it (or classify it), you need to use your heading tags on your website appropriately - otherwise when the bots crawl your website they will leave confused and not rank you as well as you might otherwise be able to rank.

Three Steps to Indexing Your Website's Content

This is just a broad overview of the steps. If you get hung up on verifying ownership of your website with Google Search Console, there are loads of videos out there on YouTube that can help walk you through step by step what you need to do. Of course, if you're working with a marketing agency or a website developer, they can assist you with this process as well.

Set Up Google Search Console

The first step to requesting that Google re-index your website is by setting up your Google Search Console. This means connecting your website with Google Search Console. Here's what you'll need to do:

Click on the three lines in the top left corner and select "+ Add Property".

You'll be prompted to select either Domain or URL Prefix. The choice is yours, but URL prefix may be easier to setup if you're doing it on your own. From here, you'll be able to select how to verify ownership of the website/URL. Some of those options include through HTML tag in which you'd upload the HTML file to your website. If you've already set up Google Analytics or Google Tag Manager on your website, those are also ways in which you can verify your site ownership.

Conduct a URL Inspection

Once you've verified ownership, you can check out your dashboard for a quick snapshot look at what's going on with your website.

If you're not sure whether your page is indexed with Google, there are one of two ways in which you can verify that it is. The first, through Google Search Console since we're already here, is to click on the tab called "URL inspection" from the left side menu. This will highlight the search bar at the top of the screen. Enter your URL in there to check whether the page has been indexed.

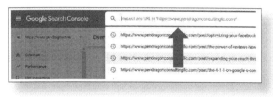

It may take a few minutes to retrieve results. If the page has been indexed, you'll get a screen that looks like this:

The second way of checking to see if your website has been indexed by Google is to type into a Google search bar:

Site: www.yourwebsite.com/pageyouwanttocheck

Obviously, that URL should be the URL you're looking to inspect. You do not have to "own" this URL to see it through this method. However, to request indexing, you do need to own it. So, head back over to Google Search Console and let's get your page indexed/re-indexed.

Request Indexing/Re-Indexing

Let's say that you've refreshed your older content to make it more relevant and timelier, or even updated one of your main pages. If that is the case, you'll want to request that Google re-index your website. To accomplish this, you'll want to click on "Request Indexing". It may take a few hours to days for Google to crawl your updated content. You don't need to click on it more than once. Just try to have some patience with it, and if it's not re-indexed by the end of the week, you can always try again.

To determine whether the Google bots have crawled your website recently, simply expand the "Coverage" tab and it will tell you the date and time the page was crawled along with the type of bot. The type of bot is important and will more often than not be a form of mobile bot as more and more users spend the majority of their time online through mobile devices. Always make sure your website and the content are mobile optimized to avoid any penalties.

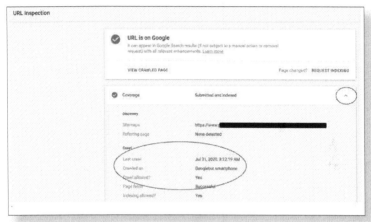

If the page is not yet on Google, you'll get a screen that looks like this:

All you have to do is click on "Request Indexing" and let the magic happen. Well, maybe not magic, but you do have to have patience while the bots queue up to crawl your website.

As you continue to index your content with website and begin a routine pace of posting new content, Google and its bots will learn the frequency and begin to crawl your website at more frequent intervals to keep up with your pace of fresh content.

Websites such as The New York Times produces content all day long. A financial planner may only update their website with a new blog once a month. Google will crawl The New York Times fairly rapidly whereas the financial planner's website may only get crawled once every few weeks - or less.

And that's that. Always make sure your content is indexed. Otherwise, all that work may be for nothing - at least until the bots learn of its existence. However, if you're going to do the work, why not make sure you get the best ROI you can get from it, especially if that means you'll be able to rank higher on Google (or the other search engines).

Chapter 11. Guest Blogging

We just finished a HUGE chapter on blogging and at this stage you may be groaning wondering how much more there can be to blogging. There's actually quite a bit more that we could say about blogging, but this is a book for beginners and so we won't continue to drone on and on about it. This chapter will be much shorter and is on guest blogging.

Blogging is for your own website.

Guest blogging is when you write an article for another website (i.e. third party) and they give you credit for it.

Ghost writing is when you write for someone else's website and don't get credit for it. If you hire a content writer for your website, ensure that your content is all ghost written. To those new to the circle of blogging, MANY businesses turn to content writers to have blogs and the writing on their website professionally ghost written. The business owner takes full credit for the writing.

Guest blogging is a great way to get your name out there and to build your company's credibility and authority. There's the word authority again. Do you remember we talked briefly about backlinks, inbound links, outbound links and hyperlinks? We talked about it in the chapter on SEO and very briefly in the last chapter if you need a refresher. Guest blogging is an opportunity for gains. These opportunities are not always easy to come by, but if you look hard enough, you'll find them.

So, what is guest blogging? Guest blogging is when you write an article/blog for a third-party website or blog to promote your own company, even if it's just by gaining a backlink. Guest blogging is frequently conducted in content marketing and for SEO purposes.

When should you consider guest blogging? Anytime you're looking for some gains! That's right, I used the word gains. Gains can come in the form of a quality backlink to help boost your DA, establishing yourself as an industry expert and to drive traffic to your website. If the third-party website you're guest blogging on gets a ton of traffic, this *could* greatly improve the traffic to your own website.

If you've decided you want to give guest blogging a go, here are a few things to keep in mind:

- Try to find websites that have at least a Domain Authority (DA) of 30 or higher.
- Every opportunity will present different possibilities.
  - Some will only allow you ONE link back to your website, others may not allow any, but may allow you to mention your company's name in the author bio.
- Guest blogging on another company's website means that you'll likely need to write about a topic that is relevant to their industry, which brings us to the next bullet point.
- Ideal websites for guest blogging should be those within your industry.
- Depending on the website, it can take weeks or even a month or two before you find out if your blog has

been accepted for guest blogging and even longer until they post it, though this is not always the case.

- Some businesses offering guest blogging opportunities will want your website to have a minimum DA of not less than a certain amount. If your website has a DA of 10 or lower, you may find more no's than yes's.

It can be frustrating trying to get a guest blog spot, but don't give up. If you wrote a blog for a website that turned down your well-crafted article, repurpose it and post it to your own website. Don't let that content go to waste!!

How to Find Guest Blogging Opportunities

Finding opportunities can prove to be a challenge if you don't know how to find them. Of course, some marketing agencies will offer you a la carte services in which they will write the article for you and get your blog posted. Fiverr, a freelancing marketplace website, may offer similar opportunities. Why pay boat loads of money, though, when you can do it for free?

Keep in mind that you're looking for *quality* links back to your website and not those riddled with spam and of poor quality. Once you find some guest blogging options, take a few minutes to check out the host's Domain Authority on Moz's free tool. It will also tell you their spam score, giving you a clear indication of whether they're worth seeking a backlink from.

Now, to find guest blogging opportunities, go head and open Google (or whatever your preferred search engine is). Now, here's what you want to do. Type in your industry followed by + write for us or + guest blog or +

guest post.

So, if I were looking for guest blogging opportunities, I might type in something like this:

Marketing + write for us

Here's what that would look like:

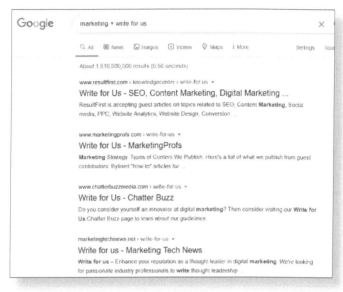

The results that Google returned are all websites that are looking for people to guest post a blog on. Let's say you're a company focused on sales. The same query would apply and look like this:

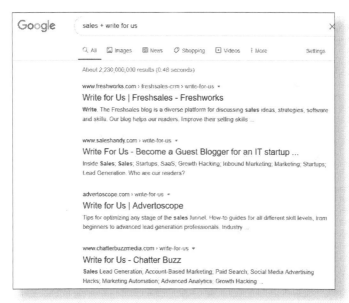

Now that you've found some guest blogging opportunities, check out their DA and Spam score. In this example, we've taken the first result from our marketing + write for us query and plugged it in to see whether they'd be a quality backlink for our site.

A DA of 36 certainly isn't considered to be of high authority (that would be a score in the 80s, 90s+), but if you're just starting out, this platform would give you a leg up and a link, so this is nothing to blink at. Their spam score is low and wouldn't really be considered a "spammy" website. So, yes, this is a great guest blogging opportunity.

No matter your industry, there's always opportunities out there if you look for them.

Chapter 12. Press Releases

If you're building a public relations strategy for your company or business (or looking for a link to boost your DA and SEO), you might have considered writing and issuing a press release. Though many people know what a press release is, very few know when and how to use them.

Read on to learn exactly what a press release is, the purpose behind releasing one, and tips to writing a profound press release.

What is a Press Release?

A press release is a written communication document that reports brief but specific information to the media. The information is usually related to an event, product launch, or any other newsworthy happening that requires press coverage. It is also great for obtaining quick keyword ranking and a valuable backlink.

The one to three pager document is circulated among media groups, with the hopes that newscasters, reporters, and editors will use the information in an upcoming radio or TV broadcast, or print it in a magazine or newspaper issue, and also on the media's webpage. Press releases are tied to an organization or a business and are delivered to media through various means.

Purpose of a Press Release

The chief use of a press release is to promote a piece of

significant and specific information clearly. Numerous situations might call for the issuance of a press release, such as:

Product Announcements: Improved products, new products, new retail outlets, and new brands entailing a product could be announced through a press release.

Company Announcement: Expansion, restructuring, new locations, relocation, new investors or financial partners, strategic partnerships are all newsworthy press releases.

Employee Announcement: Significant promotions and new hires are worthy of a press release.

Public Announcement: If there is any information that holds prominent significance or value for the public, issuing a press release would be an appropriate medium.

Awards or Honors: Special recognition or awards given to an employee, company, project, or product, are all worthy press release announcements.

Initiative Announcement: New external or internal projects that may have a considerable impact on the organization's community would be suitable for a press release.

Research Results: Publicizing the findings of a noteworthy study or survey are appropriate for a press release.

Beyond that, a press release adheres to a strict format and serves three promotional and marketing purposes:

- To inform the media about an event with the hope that they'll spread the word.
- To share something about your company, hoping a newsperson will see a story in your press release and create an actual news article about it.

- To promote your company on the internet via social networks, blogs, and websites.

The most fundamental question to ask yourself before preparing a press release is, 'who cares about this information?'; as long as the answer encompasses individuals who will go to press for this information, know that you're on the right track of issuing the press release. On the contrary, if the only people who will be interested in the information are your employees, friends, or family, you do not really require a public press release.

Key Features of a Press Release

To make it clear to reporters, editors, and writers that the information you provide them is a press release and not a letter to the editor or an advertisement, make sure you send it in a press release format. Here are some key features of a press release:

Media Contact Information: In the upper left or right corner, make sure to add the media contact information, i.e., name, email address, and the phone number of the person who the individuals should reach out to in case they have any follow-up queries.

Release Date: Below media contact information, add the date on which the report can be made public. For urgent announcements, write 'for immediate release' instead of the date. Similarly, for future releases, write 'embargoed until (add required date).'

Highlight Topic: On the left side or center of the page, write a topic headline that encapsulates the press release information. For example, 'Jack Promoted to General

Manager.'

Body of the Press Release: On the first line of the release, add the name of your city and state name in bold format and the date on which you are making the statement. For example, 'CHICAGO, ILLINOIS – May 27, 2020'. The next step is to start the announcement and encompass all the necessary information.

Write the announcement in an inverted pyramid style: mention the most essential information in the first sentence and the second most important in the next. This allows the editor to edit material from the bottom while ensuring all the crucial aspects are included.

Double Space Paragraphs: Make sure to double space the paragraphs and end the content with '###' symbols in the bottom of the center of your release.

A well-written press release sent to the right media for publication can yield thousands and even tens of thousands of dollars' worth of free publicity, and if you're lucky, a coveted link from a high Domain Authority media outlet's website to your own.

4 Tips for Writing a Press Release

Tip #1: A press release should incorporate an *attention-grabbing headline* and should always be written in the third person.

Tip #2: Make your information interesting and exciting by linking it to an ongoing trend. Nobody likes to read a monotonous piece of writing.

Tip #3: Avoid using rigid and dry wording if you do not

want to lose your audience with the first sentence. A yawn-worthy press release would do you no benefit.

Tip #4: Your press release must not be just a recitation of facts. Include quotes by prominent figures attending the event. Doing this can act as a rhetorical device to increase the interest level of the readers.

It is crucial to understand that a press release is not a definite marketing tool. Do not expect the media to jump on each press release you write. But do not give up either. Sustained and continuous efforts pave the way to achieve fruitful publicity and press releases are a vital component of a PR strategy. Thus, keep searching for ways to make your release stand out and gain enormous media coverage.

If you're a local small business, you may want to start by sending your press release to locally focused websites like Patch, a local television/radio affiliate, and regional newspapers or magazines you may see near the entrances of stores and public libraries.

Chapter 13. Leveraging Trending Topics to Your Advantage

The year 2020 has been all over the place. Is it the rule or the exception? Regardless of the answer, there are ways to get ahead of these things and turn them to your advantage. While that may sound insensitive to some, business owners who were doing everything in their power to just stay afloat understand. And that's really what marketing is all about, isn't it? You're not likely to succeed in business if you are the unknown factor. While there are some exceptions to that statement, they are few and far between.

2020 - Because How Else Do You Describe It?!

Let's take a minute to identify some of those trends in 2020 and look at the impact on the economy. We'll start with COVID-19 because the topic seems almost inescapable.

The virus was first documented in the United States in December 2019, but it wouldn't be until about the 20th of February when the stock market crashed that Americans would truly start to feel the impact of what was to come. Fast forward a few weeks to when the virus was formally declared a pandemic and would soon close down the nation with shelter-in-place orders being issued for many states, schools closing for the duration of the year, and everything deemed non-essential forced shut. It was a nationwide quarantine we will not soon forget.

Businesses were forced to come up with innovative ways to keep operations going remotely and to begin virtual offerings. Those that were able to keep up with the shift found ways to stay relevant and ultimately, to stay afloat. Restaurants began offering curbside pickups and delivery. Kid's gyms began offering lessons online. Wine and canvas shops began offering "cabin fever kits" for curbside pickup to paint at home. With an eye towards SEO, others took to the computer and hammered out enough COVID-19 content that more than tripled the traffic to their website. This was HUGE.

We talked about the power of blogs, we talked about keywords and we talked about SEO. Add in a trending topic and you have a recipe for success. COVID-19 is one of the more prevalent trending topics that had business owner's heads swiveling.

We'll move away from COVID-19 talk and into something not as widespread. In the marketing industry, we've seen some major shifts over the last few months: Google released a core update in May, Facebook published algorithm updates, Zoom came under fire for privacy concerns, Twitter was hacked, LinkedIn was accused of spying on users while its parent company Microsoft negotiated to acquire TikTok, and we can't forget the fact that the big tech CEOs from Facebook, Apple, Amazon and Google recently testified before Congress on antitrust matters. That's a lot. And kind of scary - definitely enough to give you trust issues.

"I think a lot of people really get stuck on all of the google changes. When it comes to core algorithm updates, most if not all of them are fairly mild in terms of their overall effect" says Steve from Precision Legal Marketing. "SEO industry experts, like us, spend a lot of time monitoring these changes and their affect the sites we work with, but also other sights and while impacts from these updates can be substantial at times, they don't usually wind their way down to smaller traffic sites. You need to remember that these SEO's are responsible for sites with millions of users that rank for thousands of keywords. If you are reading this, that is most likely not your situation. What I recommend is to subscribe to your favorite SEO blogs (mine happens to be Search Engine Roundtable) and take a look at it daily. They have an emailed newsletter than you can briefly read, and I don't find it to be misleading and salacious like some of the others. This way you can stay informed and keep an eye on your projects at the same time."

Leave the Cookie Cutters to the Bakers

There is no one-size-fits-all solution to marketing. What works for Company X may not work for Company Y. Similarly, what works for your direct competition may not work for you. You simply cannot take a cookie cutter approach to your marketing strategy and expect a high ROI. Not only is every industry vastly different, every business unique, but there are also several other key factors that can influence a company's marketing strategy. No matter the industry; economics and politics can always play a factor in business. It's getting ahead of those trending topics that can not only drive more traffic your way, but also establish you as a thought leader (and a leader in general) on the subject. Establishing yourself as a thought leader on a trending topic can also draw attention to your company from news outlets, giving your business a significant amount of exposure. (cough - PR - cough)

Controversial Topics: A Moment to Shine

If you're willing to broach them, controversial topics can be a great time to shine. Many businesses will shy away from controversial topics, (and depending on the topic and your industry, that may be the best thing to do) leaving a large gap - one in which you can swoop on in with your extensive knowledge to win hearts and minds with.

There's no doubt that there's enough controversy out there. Take the entire year of 2020 for example. January ushered in threats of war with Iran, gun legislation strongly opposed by 2A supporters, COVID, Black Lives Matter, Defund the Police, Aliens, Hillary Clinton's emails, the pending Presidential election, etc. In some instances, depending on your company and industry, jumping into controversial topics and choosing a side can cost you business. Always keep that at the forefront of your mind when creating content around controversial topics.

However, if you're a criminal defense lawyer who handles a lot of gun crimes, getting ahead of the competition by producing content on the *facts* surrounding the controversial topic can place you in a position of success. Well, for that topic at least. And as we mentioned earlier, this can also be a great way of gaining some free PR - as long as it's good PR and you're not coming under fire for choosing sides that ostracizes a group of people.

The best approach to producing content on controversial topics is to stick to the facts. Don't choose sides and leave your opinions on your personal pages. You do not want to exclude or ostracize a group of people with your content, and by choosing sides, you run the risk of doing just that. Check your emotions at the door.

Steve says, "Leave politics at the door too. No matter what your personal beliefs are, do not discuss them with potential customers on your website. Don't mention it all, that's not what people are on your website to learn."

Position Yourself to Become a Thought Leader

When coupled with those magical keywords, your content on these trending topics can become a mighty tool as it can help to establish you as a thought leader in your industry. (whispers - thought leader) Sounds good, doesn't it?!

While it's important to also be hitting on those areas pertinent to your industry and company as a whole, those trending topics are equally as important. It helps to show that you're not only in the know, but you're on top of your game and ahead of the competition. You can bet your last dollar that users are out there querying for those topics and if you're waiting for the dust to settle before releasing any content (such as a blog), you'll be left behind. When those individuals are querying the search engines, they're not alone - there are also news outlets out there looking to bring in experts to provide insights into what's going on.

Remember, you can always go back and update your content with new information, even make it a living document. Don't shy away from reporting information your potential customers are looking for because you're waiting until the full picture is available, or you may lose some big opportunities.

Chapter 14. Ebooks and Guides and Lead Magnets, Oh My!

Looking to build an email list or better yet, a list of qualified leads? Then you're in the right spot. In this chapter we're going to cover what exactly lead magnets are, how they work and talk about a few examples.

Let's jump right in.

What are Lead Magnets and How Do They Work?

On average, people will spend about 15 seconds on your website before leaving. You have 15 seconds or less to make an excellent impression and convince them that you're not only providing value, but you're also solving their problem or filling a need. This is where lead magnets and landing pages come in to play.

Lead magnets are exactly what they sound like: a magnet to draw leads into your sales funnel (we'll talk briefly about sales funnels in the next chapter). The magnets in this case are free resources that you're providing in exchange for contact information to build your list. Some free resources that you could offer are:

- Ebooks
- Whitepapers
- Templates
- Worksheets
- Webinars

- Other events
- Etc.

Do you see a theme here? All of those lead magnets are a form of content and therefore, content marketing. They are all also something that a potential lead may find valuable enough to give out their contact information for. Bear in mind, though, that not all lead magnets work the same.

When deciding on content and type of lead magnet, you'll want to answer a few questions. Is this something your audience will care about? Does it provide value? And more to the point, does it solve your target audience's problem? A large part of this will all come back to having a clear definition of who your target audience is.

Types of Lead Magnets

There are a number of different types of lead magnets ranging from lengthy eBooks to one-page templates. It's about knowing what your customers are looking for. Let's talk about some of the more common types of lead magnets out there.

Ebooks and Whitepapers

Among the most common of lead magnets we have the ebook and whitepaper. An ebook is short for electronic book. It is typically a bit longer than the other two. Have a collection of blogs on the same topic? Why not create an ebook with them and offer it as a lead magnet?!

An ebook can also be a guide through a process. For instance, a guide to help walk you through setting up a

Facebook Ad (check out my other book on Facebook Ads ← shameless plug). You're again not giving away your trade secrets in the guide, but rather offering enough information in it that your readers are able to accomplish a basic task with their new knowledge.

A whitepaper is a report that breaks down a complex topic, covering the background and current goings on before providing a clear and relevant solution. Whitepapers are typically more fact and statistic based, featuring things like surveys, experiments and case studies. It is definitely more technical talk than an eBook. Whitepapers hold their own appeal in providing a deeper level of understanding for the topic in question and can also build the reader's confidence in your knowledge and capabilities.

Templates and Worksheets

Templates hold their own appeal. It is a starting point that many people find themselves needing. It could be a document that provides formatting and an outline; just something to get your readers started on the topic and then fill in the blanks. I have definitely gone down the road and ended up in a few sales funnels with this one!

Worksheets are similar to templates. You're getting your readers started on whatever path they're taking. If you check out our resource section, you'll see that we are offering our own bundle of lead magnets as well (← another shameless plug). One of those is a worksheet to help you define your target audience. It's a fill-in-the-blank document that asks the question and helps you get it down on paper – and ready for your next step.

Webinars and Events

Webinars and events in general, especially free ones, are a great way to generate leads. Those on the path to success in your area's focus want to consume as much as they can along the way to better their knowledge (think here about events offered by real estate agents, financial planners, etc.). By offering to walk potential customers through something via a webinar, you're providing value, an opportunity for them to continue to grow, and perhaps even a personal connection. If you had someone sit through your whole webinar, that's more than enough to make them a qualified lead who may convert to a customer.

Other Forms of Lead Magnets

Some other forms of lead magnets include trials, product demos, virtual tours, quizzes, coupon codes and checklists to name a few. Thanks to the reopening of the economy in the wake of the COVID-19 shutdown, you can pretty much find checklists everywhere right now. Checklists to reopen your business are trending right now, to say the least.

Figure out how you can help your target audience without giving all of your trade secrets away. Whatever you come up with, make sure you give it 100 percent. If you were the customer, is this the quality or content you'd want to see?

Lead Magnet Success Tips

Put yourself in the mindset of your customer. You can do

this by looking at what's already out there. What have others with a similar industry/offering done well? What could they have improved on? *What did their customers have to say?* Check out their reviews to see what people are saying. There may not always be reviews available, but with a little digital sleuthing, you'll be able to come up with a great strategy.

Offer enough information that you've provided value and solved their problem, but not enough information that you're giving away trade secrets. Avoid straying too far in a different direction, as well as being too vague. Either path can cause someone to smash that unsubscribe button quickly.

Make sure your lead magnet is quality work. Remember that you're trying to build a list of email subscribers who will hopefully convert to customers. A document riddled with spelling and grammatical errors can lessen your credibility. Put your best foot forward by producing quality and professional looking documents to offer. If you're not confident in your magnet, ask someone with a discerning eye and penchant for honesty to give it a glance over.

Lead magnets are a powerful tool amplified by an effective landing page. When you're ready, head on over to the next chapter to learn more about landing pages.

Chapter 15. Landing Pages

While landing pages themselves aren't necessarily a form of content marketing themselves, they are a *tool* used in content marketing and can really take your marketing strategy to the next level when used effectively. These days, landing pages are an important element to lead generation online. It is a *key* opportunity to convert your website visitors into clients with a drilled down version of what they're looking for.

But what is a landing page?

What is a Landing Page?

A landing page is a page on your website that is designed to convert visitors into leads (or potentially even customers!). Typically, a landing page is used as a way of offering a resource - such as a lead magnet (i.e. eBook, guide, template, worksheet, etc.) in exchange for their contact information.

Have you ever queried the search engines on mission to find something and came across a template or other resource offered for free? Then maybe provided your name and email address in exchange for this free download? You were likely visiting that company's landing page. Despite knowing that this is a way of capturing leads to market products or services, this author is not exempt from going down the rabbit hole! In fact, I have ended up falling right into that nifty little sales funnel and converting to a customer a couple of times now. If the content is valuable, then why not?!

I know a few of you out there have likely signed up with fake email accounts, too.

Overview of the Sales Funnel

I don't want to insult anyone's intelligence here, so if you are well-versed in what a sales funnel is, feel free to keep scrolling. For those of you who aren't totally sure, don't be embarrassed. We all start somewhere. And look at you consuming all this knowledge to help you on your path to success! For real, you should pat yourself on the back for having the drive to consume as much information as you can because learning never stops. All right, off my soap box.

What is a sales funnel?

Do you remember the School House Rocks video on how a bill becomes a law? In a way, it's kind of like that saying (not the process). The sales funnel is how a lead becomes a customer. You may see the sales funnel look a little differently, depending on the source, but the concepts are all pretty much the same. There are four core concepts to the sales funnel, and they are: Awareness, Interest, Decision and Action.

The first step in the sales funnel is to build awareness - both brand awareness and awareness of the product or service that you're offering. If people aren't aware of who you are or that you offer those products or services, how can they become customers? This is why building brand awareness is so vital to your digital marketing success.

Once you've built brand awareness, the lead will become

a prospect as they enter into the interest phase. This stage takes some nurturing. What is their problem? How can your products or services solve that problem? For instance, when selling social media marketing services, you have to understand both your target audience and why that target audience may need your services. Understanding that can help you pique their interest as you continue to nurture them through the funnel.

You've worked hard to build a good impression for what you're selling and are ready to make your sales pitch, taking you into the decision phase. Getting your prospects to take the next step and make a decision isn't easy. Once you get them there, though, man is it worth it.

That takes us to the fourth phase of the sales funnel - Action. This is the phase in which your prospect takes the plunge and becomes a customer. As an enthusiastic sales professional, it's time to start the process all over again now with some new leads.

I don't want to deviate too far from the topic of landing pages and content marketing here but feel compelled to mention that a great way to build brand awareness and maintain their interest is through retargeting ads. You drive them to your website and capture their cookies - follow them across the internet like a stalker so they buy your goods. Sounds stalkery? Maybe, but it works, and brands do it all. the. time.

Steve had this to say:

> "Let me jump in here with some firm advice. Do not cheap out on your landing page design. Do not cheap out on the design of your funnel. This is not to say you need to spend some huge amount of money

building landers and funnels. You don't. But you need to build them right, and so the word cheap is not a monitory reference but rather a quality one. Make sure you understand your potential customer and not only the information about what you are selling, but what they will react to. As an example, if you are selling a skin cream, make sure you have the image of the product very near the description and a BUY NOW or some call to action nearby. Don't ask your customers to do a bunch of scrolling. Don't ask your customers to do too much reading. Once they click the buy now button, not you have them. So, think about what you (they) would want to see next. Add-ons, like products and so on. Think through the funnel process thoroughly."

The Difference Between a Lead and a Prospect

A lead is an unqualified contact, whereas a prospect is a qualified contact. What's the difference? Well, a qualified lead means that they've expressed some interest in your products or services and have started their journey through your sales funnel. A lead is someone who may or may not have expressed interest.

Expressing interest does not mean that they've reached out to you, but rather can be simply visiting your website or even filling out their contact information on your landing page in return for a valuable piece of content. Once they've expressed interest, you can begin nurturing them through your funnel.

How a Landing Page Can Benefit Your Company

Of course, lead generation is probably top of the list for many of us, but there are a number of reasons why landing pages are beneficial. Going back to our sales funnel, the first phase is awareness. Landing pages can help build awareness for your product or service that is zeroed in on exactly what your target audience is looking for. Here are some of the ways in which your company can benefit from landing pages:

- Lead generation / list building
- Brand awareness
- Increased conversion rates
- Improve paid ad campaigns

There's no set number to how many landing pages you can or should have. Create as many as you'd like and make them specific to an audience or service. It means more chances of converting your traffic into sales leads, so why not?!

Check out some of these dos and don'ts for landing pages to get you started.

Do's and Don'ts of Landing Pages

Don't Send Traffic to Your Homepage

Many businesses direct their social media, ads and email traffic (to name a few) to their homepage. This is a huge missed opportunity. Let's say your ads are geared towards a particular service that you offer, going back to social media marketing for example. Perhaps we run a

Google Ad or a Facebook Ad targeting dentists looking for social media marketing. Having a landing page that is geared towards social media management for dentists can greatly increase your chances of conversion rather than just sending that user to your homepage. Your homepage is usually very broad and not focused on exactly what you're offering and to whom.

We can say the same thing for social media and for email marketing. If you're sending out your blog or other sales emails, you want the main link to take the recipient back to exactly what they're looking for to provide value and to zero in on what they're looking for.

Do Include Key Components

You want to make sure that your landing page has a few key components to it, such as:

- The title and subtitle (don't forget your H-tags!).
- A brief description of what you're offering and how it could benefit them.
- At least one image or video (though don't overdo it, either).
- Testimonials, certifications, badges, etc. to provide proof and credibility.
- A Call to Action (CTA) - the most important component.

The CTA is typically the form in which the user would fill out with their contact information so that they could receive their free download (or whatever it is that you're offering on your landing page).

Don't Overdo It

Have you ever heard the saying "K.I.S.S. - Keep It Simple, Stupid"? That 100 percent applies here. Resist the temptation to stuff your landing page chock full of information. Keep it simple and direct. Make sure your objective is clearly defined, stating what it is that you're offering and what you want the user to do (i.e. sign-up).

In addition to keeping the amount of information minimal, you should also strive to provide an optimized user experience and avoid using any animation, which can be distracting. You want your visitors to focus on the main point of your landing page.

Do Match the Content to the Originating Source

If you've set up ads to drive traffic to your landing page, then the content of your page should match what the ad says. If your advertisement says something like "download this free resource" then your landing page should say that as well. If your landing page says test drive our software and you've led them there under the guise of a download, then you're not doing yourself any favors and are more likely to harm your efforts than to boost conversions.

Don't Ask for Their First-Born Son

Do you really need to know their eye color, name of their first born and blood type? No? Okay, so don't ask for that information. Going back to keep it simple here, only ask for the information you need - such as name, email address and depending on your industry perhaps company.

Maybe you find it beneficial to have their phone number as well. However, seeing a box filled with fields to fill out is a big deterrent and may cause them to rethink their choices. When I come across those, I find myself asking, is it worth the free download to provide them with all of that information? More often than not, the answer is no, and I move on and many others will as well.

Do Limit Navigation

The point of the landing page is to have them complete your call to action. Don't give them an opportunity to leave so easily by linking out to your homepage or other content. Limit the on-page navigation to avoid any distractions and to keep the attention on filling out that CTA form.

Landing Page Experience with Google Ads

Outside of the obvious answer of converting sales, landing pages are also the keys to a successful advertising campaign on Google Ads. You don't always have to create a special, outside-of-the-box landing page specific to each ad, but you want to make sure that the URL you're directing traffic to in your Google Ads is going to solve the user's problem (i.e. the person that clicked on your ad).

One of the metrics Google Ads looks at is the *landing page experience* and this metric directly impacts your Ad Rank.

Your Ad Rank is a value used to determine your ad's placement/ position based on whether your ad and landing page are relevant to the people clicking on your ad.

The landing page experience in Google Ads is used to

gauge how well your landing page solves the user's query. If you're not providing a quality experience and/or solving their problem, your ad may be down ranked to your competition. The better your landing page experience, the higher Ad Rank Google will assign you and your ad will subsequently be given choice positioning.

All right. I got sidetracked here. This book does not go into Google Ads, but this portion was just used to emphasize how important an optimized landing page is.

Split Testing

Split testing is also called A/B testing or A/B split testing. It allows you to compare the different versions of landing pages to see if one resonates more than the other. Some common elements that are split tested include:

- Headlines/Titles
- Wording/Content
- Images
- Layout
- CTA

Don't be afraid to create multiple versions of your landing page to see which one brings more conversions. Some reasons you may want to consider split testing are to boost engagement, increase conversions and to gain insights into your visitors.

Chapter 16. Infographics

Surely nobody wants to spend a lot of time reading and trying to comprehend pages of intricate facts and figures. It is unquestionably not a coincidence that so much of the information that we share and see online today is in some form of pictorial representation.

There is a myriad of information surrounding us that is possibly not easy to grasp or remember in the limited amount of time that we have. However, using infographics is certainly an effective way to convey complex data and figures to readers and helps them to effectively understand and absorb information promptly.

But what are infographics?

Here we've brought you a complete guide to infographics to help you understand everything about this effective information displaying tool.

What Are Infographics?

Simply put, infographics are pictorial representations of information, knowledge, or data, specially designed to exhibit complex information clearly and quickly. Moreover, they're great for improving cognition by utilizing graphics to augment the human visual system's ability to see trends and patterns.

Infographics are all about telling a story; they help readers organize data and make complex information visually digestible so that way, readers can easily and quickly process the information. Infographics are used for numerous reasons; they are concise, entertaining, eye-catching, and useful.

Infographic Components

Infographics comprise of the following elements:

- **Content Elements**: include statistics, references, and time frames.
- **Visual Elements**: involve color, reference icons, and graphics.
- **Knowledge Elements**: involves facts and figures.

Why are Infographics Used?

Usually, infographics are used for a few of the following reasons:

Create Awareness

Create brand visibility and awareness or spread the word about a vital cause.

Illustrate Data

Present facts, statistics, and figures visually using graphs, charts, and other graphic tools.

Summarize Lengthy Content

Encapsulate lengthy blog posts, reports, and videos into a bite-sized visual representation.

Draw a Comparison

Visually compare two or more services, products, concepts, features, or brands.

Simplify Complex Information

Describe complex concepts with the help of visual illustrations and cues.

How Infographics Benefit Businesses?

Infographics are very beneficial for businesses, and it greatly helps to pass on essential information to target audiences in a fun and easy way. The following are a few of the many benefits of infographics received by businesses.

Attractive and Engaging

Infographics are more engaging, and fun as compared to plain text as they generally combine colors, images, content, and movement that naturally catches the eye.

Easy to View and Scan

Most people forget a lot of what they have read and tend to have short space attention spans, but they do remember what they've seen.

Increased Traffic

Infographics are greatly sharable for use around the web. For instance, an infographic published in a WordPress blog or website usually issues an embed code. The code generates an automatic link from the original site to yours.

Boost Brand Awareness

Infographics can be used to reinforce a brand, simply because they are visually appealing. Creating an infographic embedded with your logo and with your brand prominently displayed is a powerful means of increasing brand awareness.

Search Engine Optimization

The viral nature of infographics makes people link to your site. Infographics can easily be shared on your Facebook, Twitter, Google+, LinkedIn, or Pinterest accounts, and it is there for all your followers to see.

Infographics are an entertaining, educational, and useful tool. They are an integral part of social media marketing and, more importantly, delivers vital information in a fun, engaging, and exciting way.

Infographic Tips for Success

Now that you know a little about infographics and the benefits it provides to businesses, here are few effective tips that can help you to take your visual graphics to the next level.

Tip #1: Foster Creativity and Originality

There are a plethora of visuals and infographics floating on the internet; so, if you want to get yours noticed, make sure to create something original and unique. Invest some time in research and discover what type of topics will most appeal to your target audience. Focus on questions that have been left unanswered and come up with creative ways to answer those questions.

If there is any topic that has already been covered earlier by someone else, but you still want to work on it, make sure you create an infographic with a new and fresh angle.

Tip #2: Know Your Audience

The most essential piece of homework one must do before building an infographic is to find out if it'll actually work with your target audience. Understand the type of topics your audience will prefer and the designs that will appeal to them.

The most suitable tone of the content is also crucial to determine for your audience, as that tone will be used to craft a compelling copy of the infographic. Moreover, also figure out which social media platforms are mostly used by your target audience and create an infographic that performs best on those particular platforms.

Tip #3: Incorporate Attractive Fonts and Colors

Marketers all over the world rely on color psychology and, with its help, produce designs that deliver results. If your infographic does not use fonts and colors to bring your content to life and helps to resonate with the target audience, then it might fail to stand out among other infographics present on the web.

Tip #4: Less Text, More Visual Cues

Using a lot of text can make an infographic seem uninteresting and boring. Therefore, ensure you use a lot of visual cues and a limited amount of text. One way to do this is to supplement or replace labels, subheadings, captions, and other text present in the infographic with images, illustrations, or icons.

Tip #5: Create a Visual Hierarchy

Establishing a visual hierarchy is all about arranging and organizing information on the infographic according to the order or level of importance. That way, viewers can easily scan through from one section to another. Incorporating visual hierarchy can make your infographic look attractive, professional, and cleaner.

Infographics are an excellent way to share complex information in a concise, attractive, and easy to understand way. They are gaining popularity with each passing day, and several businesses have tried to incorporate this tool in their content marketing strategies; some have flourished while others have not. If you want your name to be among the successful, make sure to follow the 'infographic tips for success' shared earlier.

Head to the back of the book for some examples of infographics.

Chapter 17. Podcasts

How would you define an audio podcast to someone who has never heard of them before? (If you haven't heard of them before, go check out our podcast: The Beginner's Guide to Marketing at https://anchor.fm/jessica-ainsworth.) This question has often surfaced on various social media platforms, including Facebook. Interestingly, but perhaps not surprisingly, the answers varied quite a bit. Although the way people define what an audio podcast differs, the responses generally overlap in the following areas:

- Radio talk
- On-demand
- Free audio shows
- Niche

So, what is a podcast?

What are Audio Podcasts?

We are not sure how many people are aware of this, but the word 'podcast' is actually a portmanteau of iPod and Broadcast.

Audio podcasting came into being as mostly an independent way for people to get their message out in the world and essentially build a community of individuals with mutual interests. But today podcasts have been adopted by organizations big and small, radio networks, comedians, TV networks, churches, storytellers and so much more.

There is not a predetermined or preplanned length, style, production level, or any particular format of podcasts. They can be split into small episodes or seasons, like what we see in a TV show or a serial.

Weekly releases of new episodes are standard, but podcasts can be released be daily, bi-weekly, or really any cadence the creator desires. In short, podcasts are generally a series of episodes.

These audio files or episodes are stored with a podcast hosting company. One of the best things about podcasts is that listeners can easily subscribe to podcast channels and get notified when the new episode comes out.

Podcasts are not only exciting, but they are also relatively very cheap and easy to produce, and anyone can benefit from the growing popularity of podcasts. You can talk about anything, or any topic that interests you, and the best thing is you don't have to rely on the radio station for its recording and broadcasting.

4 Benefits of Podcasts for Businesses

Businesses and brands can use podcasts for multiple reasons, such as sharing information about a new service or product, create brand awareness, generate more traffic, or foster relationships with the audience through engaging podcasts. Incorporating podcasts into the marketing strategy can provide several benefits to your business. Read on further to know a few of these benefits:

Fun Way to Drive Traffic

Podcasting can allow businesses to enhance their audience

to reach efficiently and quickly. This can help the company to build familiarity with a wide range of listeners. Generally, people subscribe to a podcast channel, and the chances are that as long as the audio episodes keep coming out, the audience will quite likely listen to at least some of it.

In addition to this, podcasts can also help to drive referral traffic towards your business as many listeners recommend and share podcast channels with other people who share similar interests. Thus, this can significantly aid in the company's audience reach.

Foster Connection with The Listeners

Despite being a one-sided medium, podcasts are highly effective in building relationships and connections with the audience. The listeners often feel a close connection to the person speaking on the podcast as they listen to people that share a mutual interest or common notions.

This can allow brands to build valuable relationships and foster trust; thus, listeners can be encouraged to associate themselves with the brand and lead to improved conversion rates as people are more likely to purchase something from a brand they know something about than a complete stranger.

Simple Way to Increase Brand Awareness

The consistency and familiarity of regular audio podcasts can help businesses to make their brand a household name. Businesses can integrate and relate the information about their services and products to the content of the podcast.

For instance, if you're a financial planner, then produce a podcast about stock investing or maybe retirement planning; and incorporate information about the services that you offer in that specific area. This way, podcasts can serve to be a medium of advertisement for your business.

Source of Additional Income

Connecting to the audience can help businesses to open more doors for the target audience to buy their products or services. Additionally, podcasting could also prove to be a new source for generating additional income way for the company, if the company's podcast channel is successful in acquiring sizable followers. Podcast channels that have significant followers receive sponsorships or payments by other brands for advertisement purposes.

These are just a few of the many benefits of podcasts for businesses. Thus, do not wait any longer and start your podcast channel today!

SEO Benefits of a Podcast

As a form of content, you may be wondering just how podcasts can help you rank in the search engines - because it can. Here's how you can boost your SEO while living that podcast life.

Your podcast will likely focus around one or two topics. Try to select the most relevant of keywords pertaining to the topic, just like you would in blog writing. (Do you see where we're going with this?) Once you've identified your keywords, the next step is to write about each episode. Now, there are a few ways in which you can do this:

1. Transcription
2. Blog Writing
3. Hybrid

Transcription

Not quite a hybrid, one of this author's favorite podcast's is by a company called Rank Ranger and is focused on transcription. In addition to writing regular blogs and content, they also have a podcast. In addition to the audio clip, they also provide a "here's what you can expect" overview, followed by a transcription of the entire podcast. This helps them ensure their content is not only getting out there but is helping their SEO and search engine rankings. Feel free to check out their blog section to get an understanding of what we're talking about:

https://www.rankranger.com/blog

Blog Writing

If you were to go the route of writing a blog on the podcast episode, you'll want to ensure that you're employing SEO formatting with your heading tags, keywords, alt-text and meta descriptions. In addition to proper formatting, you should make sure your blog post has a minimum of 300 words, but preferably no lower than 500 words. This is a short but sweet recap of the podcast episode that can help your rank.

Hybrid

In the hybrid method, you're looking at writing a blog, but using quotes from the transcription to cut down on the amount of writing you'll need to do.

Bonus Tip: Maximize Your SEO Success with YouTube

Second only to Google, YouTube is the second most trafficked site out there with over 1 Billion users. Ensuring that your podcast makes it to your website for SEO and traffic purposes is great, but you can really maximize your success and exposure by also getting your podcast out there on YouTube. It is both free and easy to accomplish.

Effective Podcast Tips for Success

There are a million reasons to get your podcast started today, and not a single reason not to. Having said that, there's a big difference between producing a podcast nobody listens to and producing a successful podcast that can help you with branding, marketing, and maybe even earn some big bucks.

Therefore, here are our top tips to produce and launch a successful podcast.

Tip #1: Get Decent Equipment

The initial investment in equipment is relatively insignificant as compared to the probable gains. But that does not mean you have to spend thousands of dollars on cutting-edge equipment or software. Still, you should at least have a decent microphone, a headset, and some essential editing software to ensure your podcast sounds professional and clear.

Tip #2: Choose the Right Podcast Theme

The theme of a podcast can play a vital role in determining its success. Choose a theme that you not only care about but can also commit to for the long haul. If you're genuinely passionate about what you're speaking, it will resonate with other individuals who share the same thoughts. Being genuinely interested and informed in what you choose to talk about will keep the audience engaged and the listeners will appreciate you for it.

Tip #3: Find Balance

After launching your podcast, you'll probably start receiving suggestions and comments from the listeners. Some might want you to change the format, others might request for special guests; although it is always wise to listen to the needs of the audience, it is equally important to stay true to your identity. Therefore, be in control of the podcast and steer it in the direction that can spark real conversations rather than uninteresting content. Having said that, this does not mean that you completely ignore the wishes of the listeners. Find a balance between your podcast style and the recommendations or suggestions to successfully deliver content that is loved by both you and the audience.

Shameless plug: To learn more about content marketing, or really, marketing as a whole, check out my podcast *The Beginner's Guide to Marketing*. You can find my podcast on Apple, Spotify or wherever you enjoy listening to your favorite podcast. Check out our main page here:

https://anchor.fm/jessica-ainsworth.

Chapter 18. Video Marketing

Video marketing has exploded over the past few years, and it is only going to escalate in the future. Several research pieces have shown that people retain 20 percent of what they read, 10 percent of what they hear, and 80 percent of what they see.

Video, when used in the right way, can be a perfect communication tool for brands. If done correctly, it can lead to increased sales, website traffic, and consumer engagement.

And the best part is that developing an effective video marketing strategy does not have to complicated. The key to success is to have a concrete plan and content for your video before you start.

But what is video marketing?

Continue reading this complete guide to video marketing and learn why it is crucial for businesses today to incorporate this tool into their marketing strategy.

What is Video Marketing?

If a picture is worth a thousand words, then how much more valued is a video? That is the foundation of video marketing, a straightforward marketing strategy that incorporates engaging videos into the brand's marketing campaign.

Video marketing is used for a plethora of reasons, from building customer relationships to promoting your product, brand, or service. Moreover, video marketing also serves as a medium to promote customer testimonials, present how-to's, deliver viral content, and live-stream events.

In simple terms, when a brand uses a video to market its product, brand, or service, educate current or prospective customers, interact, and engaged with them on social media channels, they are said to be using video marketing.

How Video Marketing Works?

The 'how' of video marketing seems pretty simple on the surface: brands develop a video to promote their company, raise awareness of their products and services, drive sales, and foster customer engagement. But in practice, it is a lot more complicated than this. Like many other marketing efforts, meaningful data is required to drive video marketing. Thus, brands must observe and monitor multiple metrics to track customer engagement.

To build your video marketing strategy, you must:

Allocate Resources:

You will be required to designate some budget for the video – decent equipment, a video marketing team or guru, and good editing software– and the time to create it.

Tell Your Story:

Storytelling might have never been as vital as it is in video marketing, thus start brainstorming. Figure out what stories you want to tell and how you will share them with the target audience.

Engage Audience:

It is not enough to just share your stories; you must also endeavor to foster customer engagement during the process. What will hook your target audience? How will you make the stories interesting?

Shorter is Better:

There is no fixed length for marketing videos, but the rule of thumb shows that shorter is better. Hence, be ruthless with the editing. Cut out anything that is extraneous as attention spans nowadays are short, thus make the best of what you've got.

Publish:

Once the video is ready, make sure you publish it far and wide. Embed them on your website, upload on YouTube, and on all your other social media channels.

Analyze:

Focus on stats and track metrics to determine which video performs the best and why.

How Video Marketing Benefit Businesses?

Few of the many benefits provided by video marketing to businesses are:

Improved Conversion Rates

Including meaningful videos on a landing page can boost conversion by 80 percent according to HubSpot. Watching a convincing presenter in a video can influence customers› buying behavior and compel a visitor to turn into a lead or turn a convert into a customer, compared to simply reading the same information alone.

Videos for SEO

Search engines keep looking for content that has viewer engagement capacity. Nothing entices more expansive page views than a video. Moreover, YouTube is the second leading search engine behind Google. If you put a video on your website and YouTube, your opportunity and visibility to show up in search engines is significantly increased.

Foster Credibility and Trust

Videos are a great way to create a distinct personality for your brand or company as it enables you to bond and connect with your audience and earn their trust. The more videos a brand has to help inform and educate customers, the more they'll be able to build on that base of trust. And never forget trust translate into sales.

Encourage Social Shares

This is the age of viral videos, and according to HubSpot, 92 percent of mobile video users share videos with other people. This is an excellent opportunity to have fun and show what your brand is all about. This is your chance to have some fun and really show what your company is all about. Thus, come up with video content that is relevant to your target audience.

Video Marketing Tips for Success

Tip #1: Have a Purpose

Video marketing has become so simple to practice that people often forget about the whole point of creating a video. Thus, make sure that your video has a substantial purpose. It can be anything from increasing brand awareness, encouraging sales, highlight value propositions to increasing web traffic.

Tip #2: Always Include a CTA

Always try to include some introductory text in your videos that should lead to a call to action (CTA). CTAs set up the viewer's expectation for the main content of the video. It is an introduction or a tour of the brand, product, or service.

Tip #3: Set a Video Theme

Video marketing is likely to be more successful when each video is based on a single purpose. If you feel you must include more than one topic in a single video, then try to formulate a common thread between all the different issues. Always remember that the video should serve and fulfill one ultimate purpose.

Tip #4: Don't Pitch for Sales

Generally, videos are not the place or the medium to make a sales pitch. If done the right way, the video itself will help to drive sales. But the main aim should be to offer the target audience with clear information they need to understand the product or service and ultimately lead them further into the sales funnel.

Video marketing is an excellent tool for effective communication in this digital age, especially when the span of attention of people is rapidly decreasing.

There are some really great (and affordable) tools out there to help you create some amazing videos from explainers and promotional to whiteboard and cartoons.

Chapter 19. Social Media and Content Marketing

All right so social media is its own brand of marketing. However, social media marketing does intersect with content marketing as the posts that you're creating and pushing out on your social networks are a form on content. While they both may intersect, it is important to remember that they are in fact two very different entities.

Differences Between Social Media Marketing and Content Marketing

There are three primary differences between social media marketing and content marketing. Those differences are their operations, the content, and their objectives. Let's take a closer look.

Operations

Social media marketing is conducted on the social platforms themselves, such as Facebook, Instagram, Twitter, etc. Content marketing is normally (though not always) centered around your company's website (i.e. blogs, infographics, eBooks, etc.). Social media is a great way to maximize the exposure of your website's content though.

Let's take a blog for example. Many businesses are blogging these days to help drive traffic, provide value and to ensure they're continuing to hit on those SEO keywords to rank higher. How do you get people to read your blog?

Well, you could post about it on social media and hope that people click on the link to read your article. You could also pay to boost that post on social media, displaying it to an even larger audience. What's important to keep in mind here is that the content itself is on your website and social media is a means of gaining exposure and is simply housing the link back to your website.

Content

Each social media platform has their own unique nuances when it comes to posting. Twitter, for instance, you can post up to 140 characters per post and you can include hashtags in your post to help reach a larger audience *organically*. Instagram is primarily focused on photos, but they do give you a place to include your post and again, uses hashtags to reach a wider audience with your messaging.

As the content is housed on your own website in content marketing, you have the ability to house larger content - such as blog posts.

Objectives

The two main objectives behind social media marketing are brand awareness and customer satisfaction. You want people to be exposed to your brand in order to bring in some new business. Additionally, you want to keep your customers happy and your social media pages provides them with value-driven content and a direct line of communication. It provides current and prospective clients with a way to ask questions and develop brand loyalty.

Content marketing is more focused around demand generation. You want to spark interest in what you have to offer and as they visit your website, you can begin to develop a relationship with them and nurture them towards lead conversion.

What is Demand Generation?

Demand generation is exactly what it says - a generation of demand for a business' products or services. It's a way for marketing and sales to work together to nurture prospective clients. It is a way of getting people interested *in your products or services and is not to be confused with lead generation, which is the task of turning interest into sales.*

The Intersection

Now, you may be wondering with so many major differences between the two, at what point do they intersect? Great question. The *content* itself is where social media marketing and content marketing meet. What are you posting to social media? Pictures, updates, blog links, videos, infographics, etc. Those are all examples *content* and a part of content marketing.

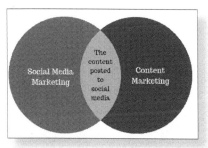

Aligning Your Strategies

Getting your content blasted out on social media is fundamental to building your brand awareness and reaching large audiences. When your social media and content marketing strategies are aligned, you've positioned yourself for a higher ROI. Some benefits of an aligned strategy include:

- Builds brand awareness
- Relevant and value driven content to current and potential customers
- Influences prospects
- Attract potential customers
- Drives traffic to your website or landing page
- Return at every stage of the sales funnel
- Client retention
- Customer satisfaction

With social media, you're able to meet potential customers before they are even in the market for your product or service. One in three people were active on social media networks in the last year, making social media crucial to your brand's online success.

Conducting Research

Who is your target audience? What common interests do they have? What keywords are they using to find you and other businesses in your industry on the search engine? What questions are they asking? Understanding the answer to those questions can help shape your content marketing strategy and determine which platforms your company should be marketing on. Unless you're running paid advertisements, social media accounts are free to create and maintain. So, what have you got to lose?

Establish KPIs to Measure Your Success

What Are KPIs?

KPIs stands for Key Performance Indicators and they are set of quantifiable measurements used to gauge a performance.

Measuring Success

When aligning your social media and content marketing you're looking to build awareness for your brand, drive traffic to your website, boost engagement for your page and increase conversions. How do you measure the success of each of those to know whether your strategy is working or if you need to shift focus? Through your KPIs.

Awareness

The two key metrics you can use to measure whether you've been successful in building brand awareness through your social media efforts are through the number of impressions and the number of people reached.

Impressions are the total number of times people have seen the content. Reach is the total number of unique profiles that your content has been shown to. You see, one person may have seen your content three or four times, meaning chances are pretty good that your reach will be much lower than your impressions.

Drive Traffic

When looking to measure the success of this goal, some KPIs you'll want to consider are website clicks. This tells you how many people have clicked on the link to your website from the post. If you've got your Facebook Pixel installed correctly, all of those people will have been caught in your Pixel's web so you can retarget to them later on.

Boost Engagement

Engagement is measured through things like "likes", comments, shares, pageviews, social mentions, followers and sessions. No one KPI will tell the whole story. They are all unique pieces of a puzzle and when put together can give you a more accurate visual of whether you've been successful in boosting engagement.

Increase Conversions

The money maker and goal we're all trying to accomplish - increasing conversions. This success of this stage will be determined by your website. You can use Google Analytics (if you have the code installed on your website) to help you track who was on what page, how long did they spend and what page did they visit next. While aligning your social media and content marketing strategies, did you notice an increase in blog subscribers? Increased traffic to your product or service pages?

Using Insights to Provide Insight

See what we did there? Yup, this author is a total nerd.

Each social media platform typically has a version of analytics that you can use to help gauge some of those KPIs without having to dig very far.

- Facebook Insights
- Instagram Insights
- LinkedIn Analytics
- Twitter Audience Insights

Each of those platforms offer a bird's eye view of KPIs. *This is only available for company pages and not for individual profiles.*

Measuring the KPIs isn't as difficult as it probably sounds and if you're going to do something, isn't it worth it to do it right the first time?

Determine Your Strategy

Your strategy for aligning your social media and content marketing can help improve your ROI and maximize your company's effectiveness.

Audit Your Current Social Media Pages

Before you get started, you really need to do a run through of your company's current social media pages. Here are some things you'll want to keep an eye out for:

- What social platforms is your company on?
- Are there any duplicate pages?
- Is the information on your pages accurate and up to date?
- Are all of the fields filled out in their entirety?
- Are your pages all uniform? (i.e. they all look the same to promote brand awareness/brand recognition)
- Remove any inactive accounts.
- Ensure the social links on your website are 1) there and 2) correct.

Ensuring your pages are optimized before you start working on boosting engagement can help you put your best foot forward. An inaccurate or incomplete page may give the impression that you're lazy or unprofessional. Yes, it is that serious.

Define Your Target Audience

We talked about this briefly a bit earlier in this chapter. Based on who your target audience is, what type of content should you be producing? How will you capture their attention? What social platforms are your target audience using? Those are the platforms that you want to be on as well. For instance, if your target audience is primarily using Facebook, then that should be your primary focus when it comes to social media.

Establish Brand Personality, Tone and Voice

Understanding *who* you are marketing to, can help you

shape *how* you talk to them (i.e. brand personality, tone and voice). An older generation may not be up on the latest hip new slang whereas the younger demographic might be. Identifying the right tone can help you maintain a consistent message across the various platforms.

When companies make the decision to rebrand, this may also mean rebranding their tone. An awesome example of this is Wendy's. They went from meh to a HUGE following in Twitter with awesome Tweets that will have you rolling on the floor with laughter. Seriously, go check out Wendy's on Twitter - you won't regret it.

Research the Competitive Landscape

Scope out your competitor's social media accounts. What platforms are they using? How many times a week are they posting? What kind of content are they posting? Is it working? Knowing this can help you determine what *is* working and what's *not* working for them so you can take the best and the worst to help shape your own strategy.

Build a Social Media Content Calendar

Arguably, this may be the most fundamental step in a successful social media strategy. It helps you plan ahead, stay organized, maximizes efficiency and leads content creation.

Conduct Periodic Reviews

Just because you've checked all of the boxes doesn't mean you're done. People change. The economy changes - some years more than others (*cough* 2020 *cough*). By conducting periodic reviews you're able to identify if anything needs to be changed to meet the new demands. There will come a time in the not so distant future that you'll need to adjust your strategy. It's like shampoo bottles say - lather, rinse, repeat. Only in this case, it's audit, define, establish, research, calendar, repeat.

Chapter 20. What Social Platforms Should Your Business Be Using?

It seems like there are new platforms popping up all the time. The newest trending platform being Parler (pronounced par-lay; not to be confused with the dating app Parlor). With all of these social platforms out there, how do you know which platforms your company should be using to push out your awesome content through social media marketing? Well, it all comes down to narrowing down who your target audience is and then taking a look at the various demographics using the different social platforms.

Defining Your Target Audience

This is a big one because not everyone is your client or will be your client. Say it with me folks: **Not everyone is your client.** We talked about how to define your target audience earlier in the book. In order to determine which social platform(s) your business should be marketing and/ or advertising on, you need to understand just *who* you're marketing to. Advertising will allow you the ability to really narrow down your audience by demographics, but for just maintaining a presence, you don't need to have as a precise of an idea.

For instance, if you're a financial advisor, your target audience may be older adults seeking to retire soon. Or perhaps even the younger CEOs out there in their mid to late 30's, who also tend to be predominately male. You may not find the older demographic on Instagram or Twitter as much but may rather find them on Facebook where the fastest growing demographic is 55+. The younger CEOs on the other hand may be easier to market to on other platforms - such as LinkedIn and yes, even Facebook.

It's all about figuring out which platform your potential clients might be and maintaining a presence on them to maximize your Return on Investment for social media marketing. Keep in mind that you may not find leads as fast as you're hoping without some form of paid advertising to build brand awareness because if they don't know who you are, how will they convert to a customer?!

Facebook

By far the largest of all social networks, Facebook boasts 2.41 *billion* (yes, you read that right) monthly active users. For global ranking and visibility, this social platform takes the third position as the most visited website *globally*, outranked only by Google and YouTube. Of those users approximately 10% of the total users are American and approximately 71% of American users are adults.

Facebook usage varies slightly by gender with 63% of men using the platform compared to 75% of women users. In addition to the differences in genders, we can also identify a wide disparity amongst age demographics:

- 18 - 24: 76%
- 25 - 29: 84%
- 30 - 49: 79%
- 50 - 64: 68%
- 65+: 46%

Those numbers may be lower for older Americans, but

don't let that fool you. Seniors are the fastest growing group of Facebook users. In fact, eMarketer predicts that Facebook will see a 7% growth in the 65+ demographic. Older demographics of 50-64 come with a higher net worth and income, which is probably what you are interested in.

Are you looking to market to a wealthier demographic? Facebook has you covered there as well with 74% of high-income earners maintaining profiles on the social platform.

Should your company be marketing on Facebook? Quite frankly, this is the one platform that is almost essential for businesses regardless of industry.

LinkedIn

Coming in as the fifth most popular social media platforms in the U.S., there are 675 million monthly active users. While 70% of LinkedIn's users are located outside of the U.S., a whopping 167 million users are based out of the U.S. That's approximately 27% of Americans.

Of the 167 million Americans using the social platform, 57% of LinkedIn users are men and 43% are women with a collective total of 61% of users being between the ages of 25 and 34 years old.

With LinkedIn being a platform for professionals, this is a sure win for those companies in the B2B realm. This does not mean that those a B2C focus should steer clear of marketing on LinkedIn, if your demographic lines up with those using LinkedIn, we absolutely recommend using this social network.

Twitter

In Q1 2019 Twitter announced that they had over 330 million monthly active users. Of those, there are approximately 145 million monetizable daily active users. What does that mean? That means that of the 330 million monthly active users 145 million are users that login daily and can see advertisements across their feeds. Of those 145 million, 30 million daily users are American. 44% of U.S. based Twitter users are between the ages of 18 to 24 years old.

There are some businesses that just don't see the relevance in marketing their companies over Twitter. Other law companies are finding much success in getting their name out there. It all comes down to who you are marketing to. Our advice is this: If you're already putting together content for other social platforms, **why not copy + paste it to Twitter as well?** As with the rest of the social networks, Twitter allows your company to maintain a social profile for free. So, what do you really have to lose?

Twitter and Instagram are both great platforms that allow you to really expand your organic reach through the use of hashtags. Not only that, but you can also find topics that are trending in your area (and nationally) to jump in on and get a little extra exposure for.

Instagram

There are approximately 1 billion monthly active users on Instagram with 110 million being located in the United States. That brings us to approximately 37% of American adults using the social platform. Instagram is by far more popular among younger demographics with 67% of users being between ages 18 - 29. 62% of users say they have become more interested in a brand or product after seeing it in Stories.

Like all previously mentioned platforms, Instagram is free to join. This platform is focused on photos, meaning you have to have a photo to post on this platform. One major bonus to marketing on this platform is that, like Twitter, you're able to use hashtags to reach a larger audience organically.

On Facebook, your posts will reach about 1.6 - 2% of your page's followers depending on the level of engagement. The more people engage, the more your post will be shown to. When coupling your content with valuable hashtags that people are *actually* looking at, you can really maximize your organic reach. This doesn't mean that you should throw in a random hashtag that no one is looking at or for. For instance, if we were to post about a content market statistic with an amazing Rockstar image of something content related, we might include hashtags such as: #marketing #digitalmarketing #b2bmarketing. Some hashtags we would not be inclined to use include: #pendragonrocks. No one is looking at or for #pendragonrocks and so there is no value in that hashtag.

YouTube

Looking for a platform that outperforms all others? Look no further. YouTube ranks number one for social media platforms. YouTube has over 2 billion monthly users and is on track to continue growing. 73% of American adults use this social platform, making it the most popular social platform in the United States. While the largest number of users stems from the age bracket of 15 - 25 years old, all other age brackets give that demographic a run for its money. At the lowest rate, 58% of those ages 56+ use YouTube.

Even the other platforms (such as Facebook) have come to prioritize videos over regular content. What does this mean for your company? It means you should really consider having some videos made to post to YouTube (and to other social networks) to work on building your brand awareness and following.

Social media marketing is a long-haul effort unless you're paying to advertise. You're working towards building brand awareness and brand recognition with your current and potential clients. Not everyone will need your product or services today, but they might tomorrow, and you want your company's name to be the first that comes to mind when that day comes. Whatever platform you choose to market on, social media is a necessary beast these days as it not only expands your reach into new potential customers but also helps to build brand awareness as well as credibility. Take your social media marketing efforts to the next level by determining your target audience and getting your company listed on the relevant social platforms.

Looking for a social media cheat sheet to refer back to? Hop on over to our website

https://www.beginnersguidetomarketing.com/
contentmarketing

to download your free resources - including a social media cheat sheet infographic - today!

Chapter 21. Optimizing Your Company's Social Presence

Over 70 percent of the U.S. population holds a social media account on at least one platform. If you're looking for a free way to reach the masses, this is it. In fact, it's almost essential these days for businesses - regardless of industry - to have a social media page in the modern digital world.

As we've already covered the basics of *why* social media and *how* it fits into the content marketing equation, let's look at some best practices and ways of optimizing your company's presence.

Social Media Best Practices

As with everything, there are some best practices to be mindful of when establishing your presence on social media.

DO remain consistent across the platforms. Many companies choose to create business profiles on a variety of platforms such as Facebook, LinkedIn, Twitter and Instagram. Your profile picture, cover photo, description, contact details, etc. should all be exactly the same across each platform. This can help create brand recognition and brand awareness as well as demonstrating quality and professionalism.

DO complete your profiles. Don't skimp on the details or leave anything blank. Provide as much information as you can to ensure your audience has enough to make an informed decision.

DO post regularly. Posting to your social accounts 2 - 3 times per week is a great number. Anything more than that may be seen as excessive and could result in your company's page being "unliked" or "unfollowed". Although, the number of posts per week is a general guideline and not a rule. Conduct competitor research to see what's working for them and what's not to help you figure out how often you should be posting.

DO hashtag research. Obscure hashtags that aren't used by many people will fall on deaf ears, meaning no one will see your post. In the search bar of LinkedIn, Twitter and Instagram you have the ability to search for hashtags and the results will tell you how many posts have been made with them. The more that's posted to it, the more views that content is getting. For instance, #marketing has a *big* following but #yourcompanyname will likely have almost no results.

DO provide relevant and timely information. Use this as a way to spread industry news. If your law firm's primary practice area is personal injury and we just hit the summer months, posting about motorcycle accidents and dog bites, things that people are looking for right now, can be a great way to drive engagement.

DON'T be disappointed with low organic reach. Only 1.6 to 2 percent of your followers will see your organic posts. A great way to boost these numbers is by getting people to engage with your posts. The more that engage, the more the post will be shown to.

DON'T post irrelevant content. Your company's social media page shouldn't post on things such as Hollywood drama or fashion. These topics may be a great way of getting engagement, but you're attracting people who are *not* likely to convert to clients thereby defeating the purpose of social media marketing.

Consider Advertising

A great way to expand your reach *and* to draw in new, qualified leads for your business is through advertising on social media. Facebook, for instance, allows you to create forms that potential clients can fill out with their information. Those results then populate in an Excel form that you can download and provide to your sales team to contact.

Social Media Advertising can also help you build up your followers and drive engagement. For businesses just starting out on social media, this may be a great way to build your company's following.

With millions of people using social media in the United States, your company can't afford to miss out - especially since creating business pages is totally free. Once you define your target audience, you can figure out which platform may be best suited towards your needs. Currently, Facebook has the largest number of users and is a fan favorite for advertising however, you should consider establishing a presence on each of the platforms as they're free and you never know where you may find your next client.

Optimizing Your Facebook Business Page

There are six basic steps to optimizing your business page on Facebook and they are:

1. Select the right type of page
2. Custom username
3. Images
4. Fill out all of your details - Don't leave any blanks!
5. Ensure your contact information is accurate
6. Remove/hide unused tabs

Let's walk through those six steps.

Select the Right Type of Page

When you first create your Facebook business page, you'll be able to choose from a variety of options such as:

- Local business or place
- Company
- Brand or Product
- Public Figure
- Entertainment
- Cause or Community

By selecting the right type of page from the onset it can help enhance the way you communicate the message your company wishes to show.

Create a Custom Username

You have the ability to create your own username. For instance, on Facebook the Pendragon username is @ pendragonconsultingllc (so, go follow us!). However, if you'd like something different or want it to match other social accounts who don't offer the ability to be choosy, you do have some flexibility there. We've noticed in some cases that those who don't create a username for their page just don't end up with one at all. So, make sure that you've checked the box and create a custom username for your business page, so you don't end up with a random string of alpha-numeric characters for your Facebook slug.

Images

All right. Now, what picture should you post for your business? Your hot new product? The CEO of your company? A staff photo? Logo? While the answer may differ depending on your brand and industry, the majority of businesses favor using their logo. This can really help you create brand awareness and brand recognition for your company. The trick to your profile and cover image is consistency. Again, in an effort to foster brand recognition and brand awareness you want to present a consistent brand across your digital marketing efforts such as social media platforms and on your website.

Fill Out All Your Details - Don't Leave Any Blanks!

All right. This is one of the most common issues we run across when we take over the social media marketing for our clients. Either missing or inaccurate information throughout their business page. Ensure that you input as much as you can into your profile such as your contact information, set your categories (what industry are you in?), your about section, "our story" and even your open hours. Not only does this help users find you easier, but it also helps to instill confidence in the fact that you're a professional organization not taking a half-hearted approach. Incomplete or inaccurate profiles may be a negative sign to potential buyers, indicating that you cut corners (though not always).

Ensure Your Contact Information is Accurate

This is not only important so that your potential customers can find you, but also for local SEO purposes. Counting as a directory listing (aka citation) you want to ensure you have accurate information to promote your local SEO and to avoid being downranked. If Google and the other search engines aren't clear on your correct contact information so as to provide accurate information to their users, they may end up downranking your website.

Remove/Hide Unused Tabs

While you won't have the ability to turn off *all* of the tabs, you do have the ability to turn off a bunch of them. If they're not relevant and/or you're not using them, turn them off so they don't appear on your business page. Just one step closer to having that spiffy, professional page that demonstrates your brand's level of quality.

Linking Instagram to Your Facebook Page

Now owned by Facebook, Instagram is yet another free social networking site for you to capitalize on. You have the ability to simultaneously post to both Facebook and Instagram by linking your accounts. You can accomplish this by click on Settings from your Facebook Business Page and then clicking on Instagram on the left side menu.

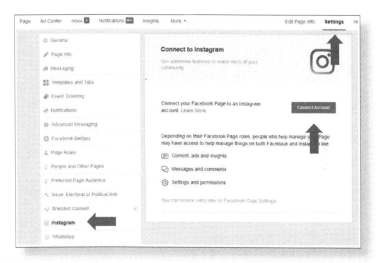

Once you've clicked on the Instagram tab, click on the blue button labeled "Connect Account". During this process you'll be asked to provide your username and password to login to your Instagram account in order to establish the connection. You may also be asked to upgrade to a business account as many people sign-up initially as individuals and not businesses. That's it. It's really just that simple.

Optimizing Other Pages

Once you've completed your business page and all of your information is accurate and filled in, you can then move on to optimizing your other profiles as well. Not to say that you *have* to start with your Facebook account, but whatever account you choose to start with, make sure that the information you put out there is consistent across all profiles, pages and accounts.

Social Media Advertising

Social media networks, like Facebook, give you the ability to advertise to expand your reach into new pools of individuals. If you're creating content such as kick butt blogs, you'll want to make sure you're driving traffic as best you can to those blogs. Advertising on social media is a great way to do that. In addition to helping you build brand awareness and drive traffic to your website, you're also able to conduct lead generation through having individuals fill out forms to qualify them, taking your marketing and lead generation efforts to the next level. Bear in mind that social media advertising is so much more than just boosting a post.

Chapter 22. Repurposing and Refreshing Older Content

You are a content marketing whiz kicking out four blogs a month and a boat load of other relevant pieces to boot. That's 48 blogs per year. You know how they say search engines love continuously updated websites? Well, they probably love yours. And if you're playing the game right with your long-tail keywords, I bet by the end of your first year you've seen some big gains.

But man, 48 blogs per year and let's say you've been doing this for 3 years. That's 144 blogs. Do you really think that 1) people are going to go back that far and 2) if they do, that it will still be relevant and timely? Also, let's not be coy here... your SEO game probably wasn't that strong as it is now and even if it was, with all of algorithm updates and the ever-evolving landscape of what people are querying search engines for, it's not likely doing you any favors as it sits there growing stagnant and dusty.

So, what can you do about it? Refresh it. And if it needs more than a face lift, scrap it and redirect it. Let's jump in a bit more here.

Boost Your SEO with Recycled Content

You want to play the SEO game in an effective manner? Refresh your old content with relevant and timely information throwing in those hot long-tail keywords that will put you on the map. This is one of the quickest wins you can get.

Building backlinks, creating content, ranking for keywords, they all take time, like at least several months of time. We already talked about how SEO is the long-haul effort to ranking and in a steady, unpaid manner. By refreshing your older content, you can give your content a rankings boost in as little as a few weeks.

One of the factors in Google's ranking algorithm is how fresh your content is. The older it is, the staler it becomes, and Google does not want to dole out page one ranking to stale content. The more relevant and fresher your content is, the more Google will see it as being *quality* and will keep you ranking. The top results of a Google search query typically show results from the past year or so.

When running your own queries, don't you want to see the most current information out there? Things can change quickly, and you want to know that you're reading what the most current and up to date information is so that you have an accurate answer to your question.

Once you've refreshed your content, don't forget to ask Google to re-index it, letting Google know that you've updated the content and their bots need to check out how fresh your website is. So fresh and so clean, clean. (Did you sing it? If not, we can't be friends. J/K)

Here are a few tips to repurposing and refreshing your older content:

Pride in Content

It's not simply an update of the date that Google and your readers are looking for. You don't want your readers to click away as soon as they read the first bit. Neil Patel says, "Great search results are based, in part, on how valuable people find your page." This means updating your content with a purpose. Don't just update the basics. Make your content more relatable. Use the power of storytelling to capture your audience's attention and leave them coming back for more.

Pride in content also means combing your work for any spelling or grammatical errors. We all know how much it can diminish the professionalism you've worked hard to build with a misuse of the word *your* and *you're* or *there* and *their*. Take the time to reread your work to ensure it is up to the highest of standards. If your grammar isn't the best, you can always ask a friend or co-worker to look over your work before republishing it. The fact of the matter is that typos and errors may not impact Google's ranking algorithm, but they do negatively impact the user experience, and Google places special emphasis on providing exceptional user experiences.

Delete as Needed

Your content isn't always going to be relevant at a later date and perhaps there's not a whole lot to be salvaged. If you find this is the case, delete it. I know that's a hard pill to swallow. You've worked hard to produce content and done your keyword research in order to rank for certain words. However, Myspace isn't going to make a comeback, so blogs on Myspace can surely be deleted.

If you are going to delete a blog, make sure that you create a 301 redirect to the most relevant page, so you don't end up with any broken links. For instance, if your page was talking about marketing on Myspace, consider redirecting the page to another page dealing with social media marketing, closest in content to the blog you're deleting.

Fix Broken Links

Demonstrate your website's value by fixing any broken links on your website. Check your site for broken links by using this awesome (and free) tool to search for broken links on your website:

www.brokenlinkcheck.com

If you do have any broken links, either fix them so they are going to the appropriate website or simply remove the link from your page. Bear in mind that you want at least one outbound link in your blog (not web copy) to someone else's website/content. So, if this is the only link in that blog, you'll want to supplement it with another link.

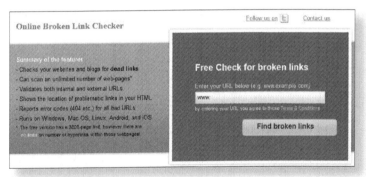

We're all about the Chrome Extensions, so another great tool is the Broken Link Checker Extension on Google Chrome.

Up Your Multimedia Game

What I mean by that is, if your blog doesn't have any visuals such as images, videos, infographics, etc., then you're missing out on some opportunities. Not only will your content be considered visually boring, but you'll also be missing out on potential pools of traffic from Image Searches and Video searches. Salesforce reflects that you should use one visual for every 350 words on your website and that blog posts with more images attract more backlinks. Of course, your visuals/multimedia should all be relevant to the topic and include a link to the original source (if you didn't create it). Don't forget to use the Alt Text to describe each image you insert.

Keyword Optimization

What users are typing into the search engines to find your company or your competition may not be the same words or phrases they use a few months from now. When refreshing your content, you'll want to check to make sure your keywords are still relevant. If not, dig around a little bit to find the right keywords to optimize your content with.

If you need a refresher on conducting keyword research, feel free to zoom back to the chapter on proper keyword research to ensure you're maximizing your efforts.

Merge Duplicate Content

If you have content that's relatively similar, merge the content into one big, all-encompassing masterpiece that covers all four corners of the topic. It is better to have one giant article that covers A - Z of a topic than to have a little bit here and a little bit there with a lot of overlap/duplicate content.

Share It

After refreshing and requesting your page be re-indexed, don't forget to share it! Blast it out on those social networks and promote it just like the rest of your content. Make sure your blogs all have share links on them to make it even easier for your readers to share those awesome posts. Sharing and promoting your content can help you expand your reach and maybe even acquire some new backlinks for your website, further boosting your SEO efforts.

Chapter 23. Creating an Effective Content Marketing Strategy

One of the most asked questions by aspiring marketers and business owners alike is how to build an effective content marketing strategy or plan. Many people assume that the key to creating an effective content marketing strategy is hidden behind special tricks or secrets. But the truth is there are no secrets.

Instead, an effective content marketing strategy simply demands plenty of time and meaningful effort, along with a proven seven-step framework as a guide. The seven fundamental steps offer the quintessential framework for long-term success.

In this chapter, we will discuss the seven steps of creating an effective content marketing strategy.

Why is Content Marketing Strategy Important?

Before we dive straight into the chapter, we first want to emphasize that a content marketing strategy is not a 'nice to have'; rather, it is an essential driver to achieve success. The Content Marketing Institute confirms in their Annual Benchmarks, Budget and Trends Report that marketers who have a well-thought and documented content strategy are far more successful than marketers who fail to have one.

This is precisely why we have put together this guide; to help you reach your highest marketing potential with a proven 7-step framework to creating an effective marketing strategy.

Benefits of Content Marketing Strategy for Marketers

Here are some real benefits that marketers receive from a content marketing strategy.

Improved Content Marketing ROI

Marketers can identify and refine tactics that are most appealing and motivating to high-quality leads. This way, they'll invest only in content that works and either eliminate or reduce content that isn't producing expected results.

Determine Content ROI

Only with a documented content strategy can marketers produce the parameters to get an idea of how successful and effective their content marketing is.

Augment Customer Segmentation

With an appropriate content management system, marketers can personalize their content for diverse segments. This is an integral key to boosting conversions and retention rates.

More Revenue & Less Churn Rate

Using a content strategy can allow marketers to have a better idea of what their customers seek. This will help them to boost long-term revenues and reduce churn rates.

Leverage Marketing Tactics

By developing a long and short-term plan, marketers can see ten steps ahead into the future. For instance, pulling off a brilliant influencer marketing campaign in three months and planning for a mega branding conference in 3 years.

Improved brand reputation, social media optimization, higher customer acquisition rates, and ultimately becoming a better marketer are few of the other benefits of creating an effective content marketing strategy.

7-Steps to Creating an Effective Content Marketing Strategy

To help you get started and level up your content efforts, here is a brief overview of the seven steps to creating an effective content marketing strategy:

Step #1: Document Goals

It can be very easy to get caught up in the where, what, and how of content marketing, which often leads marketers to skip over the single most essential foundational piece: the why.

Hence, ask yourself, why are you doing content marketing? To build relationships? To generate leads? To improve customers' experience?

Regardless of your content marketing targets, just ensure they are sustainable for the long-term and connect to your business's overarching objectives, mission, and vision. To make your strategy crystal-clear and focused, we recommend you stick to a maximum of three to five business goals and make sure to document them.

Always remember that creating content just for the content's sake should never be your goal.

Step #2: Set Yourself Apart

There is a myriad of content out there, and with each passing day, more and more are being published. So, what type of content can you create to set your organization apart from other players in the market? Simply put, what is the heart and soul of your content marketing strategy? Is it to:

- Create a utility?
- Inspire and motivate?
- Entertain and educate?

The only fitting response to all of the above is YES! Or else, you may run the risk of delivering more of the same and add to that massive, growing content glut.

Step #3: Measure Content Marketing

If you want to track your content progress, do something trackable, and determine the metrics that can prove the viability of the content, even before you create it.

To understand if the content is really doing what it is intended to, you need to look to action and not just eyeballs. This is where the four categories of content marketing metrics come in play:

1. **Sales Metric:** Did you generate any money from this piece of content?
2. **Consumption Metric:** What did the audience do with the content? Consider their actions: downloads, views, visits, listens, etc.
3. **Lead Generation Metric:** How many leads a piece of content is generating?
4. **Sharing Metrics:** How resonant is the content, and how frequently is it shared with others?

Step #4: Identify Top Audience

Often marketers forget that the created content is not for them. It's for their audience. Thus, they must focus on the motivations and needs of the audience, rather than themselves.

Relevancy automatically grabs time and attention. To be relevant, marketers need to understand who they're targeting and talking to. Few versions of what that looks like are:

Audience: High-level groups of motivated individuals with a mutual plan or interest, such as repeat product purchasers.

Segment: Cross-sections of a population or an audience that shares one or more mutual traits or can be categorized by a common attribute such as work-from-home parents.

Persona: A detailed, data-informed, and yet conjured characterization of the behavior and goals of a hypothesized faction of users.

Whichever audience you lean towards to guide your

content marketing efforts, ensure that you focus only on your top five audiences. Look at their demographics and psychographics and plan the strategy accordingly.

Step #5: Research Audience Needs

It doesn't matter which tactic you use to categorize and identify your customers from step 4, But to know them better, use the 5x5x5 methodology.

This approach takes your top five audiences, looks at their top five questions at each of the five main stages of the marketing funnel. This helps marketers better understand the needs, wants, and expectations of their top audiences and create content that fulfills it all.

The 5x5x5 method can allow you to know your target audience much better and determine where your content stands with helping them. One of the main features of an effective content marketing strategy is not just to fulfill business goals but also to answer the audience's queries.

Step #6: Less is More

When it comes to content tribulations, almost everyone thinks that the solution is to create more. But as discussed earlier, there's a glut of content out there, and you must avoid adding your content to that already massive heap.

Moreover, you might have created enough content by now; thus, try to refresh or remix your content before planning to create a new piece. Consider reusing or repurposing and curating old content. Focus on customer-generated content or content atomization to use existing work in a more lucrative way.

Remember that content is not free. Hence, maximize what you already have and only then move your efforts towards creating a new copy.

Step #7: Develop a Content Calendar

Content calendars are a shareable resource used by teams to plan content activity. This can allow marketers to visualize how their content is distributed throughout the year.

A calendar-based format is more ideal for this purpose as opposed to building a long list of content to be published. A content calendar can allow you to achieve cross and inter-department alignment, a clear view of the content distribution, identify critical milestones, and spot potential content gaps.

Ready, Set, Write!

Creating an engaging, rewarding, and long-term content strategy is not an easy task, but if done correctly with shot and long-term objectives in mind, it is going to pay off. If it's overwhelming, do not forget that you are not just pushing another product or adding to the noise; you are a storyteller sharing your company's story that deserves to be heard.

Additionally, based on the insights from your established metrics, it's crucial to refine your content strategy throughout its life. A simple general rule of thumb is: whatever is not working, do less of it. Whatever is working, do more of it. To be a successful content marketer, you should be flexible enough to test and experiment with new things and know when to stop.

Afterword

All right. We have just imparted a bunch of knowledge here. More than enough to get you started on creating some boss content.

My advice to you is this. Always take the time to do it right the first time. Do your keyword research, optimize for search engines, create your content to be valuable to your *customer* and most importantly, define your target audience. Not everyone is your customer. Understanding that and knowing who fits the mostly likely to convert to a paying customer demographic can greatly maximize your Return on Investment.

We all make mistakes. So, if something isn't working, don't lose all hope. Shift your focus and try again. Failure is the ladder to success.

I hope this book has provided you with a stepping point and has demystified some areas of contention. On behalf of myself and all of us with Pendragon Consulting, we wish you much success on your journey to create effective content.

And don't forget to download your FREE gifts to help you continue along your journey!

www.beginnersguidetomarketing.com/contentmarketing

Additional Resources

We talked about some great resources in this book that I wanted to compile to share with you. These are all tools that I've mentioned throughout this book. I am not being paid to share any of these resources, with the exception of SurferSEO in which I may receive a very small commission if you use my link - and I use SurferSEO and LOVE it (not just because I get paid to say it!).

SurferSEO -
https://surferseo.com/?fp_ref=jessica53

Surfer SEO takes a scientific approach to on page SEO. It helps make getting your page to rank much easier, faster and more efficient all the while utilizing data-driven, real-time guidelines. SurferSEO also offers a Chrome Extension that you can download for free, giving you a broad understanding of the search volume of keywords. This extension is called KeywordSurfer.

HubSpot Academy -
https://academy.hubspot.com/

Earn some boss marketing certifications for free through HubSpot Academy. Topics range from content marketing, social media marketing, inbound marketing, SEO, WordPress, YouTube, and all things marketing.

MOZ's Free SEO Tools -
https://moz.com/free-seo-tools

Explore keywords, links and more - for free - with Moz's free SEO tools. Take a look at your Domain Authority (DA) to help you determine where you may need to improve.

Google Search Console -
https://search.google.com/search-console/welcome

Ensure that your content is indexed with Google through the Google Search Console. This is also where you would request indexing, if needed.

Pendragon Consulting's Blog -
https://www.pendragonconsultingllc.com/blog

Our company, Pendragon Consulting, produces a weekly blog chock full of information and resources on all things marketing.

Precision Legal Marketing -
https://precisionlegalmarketing.com/

If you are a lawyer or law firm seeking to maximize your ROI through marketing, Precision Legal Marketing can take you there with fully customized solutions tailored to the needs of your law firm.

Broken Link Checker -
www.brokenlinkcheck.com

A free tool to check whether your website has any broken links. They also have a Chrome Extension that you can install to make it even easier to find broken links.

SEMrush -
https://www.semrush.com/

An all in one paid SEO platform to help you kick butt and rank like a boss.

Rank Ranger -
https://www.rankranger.com/

An all in one SEO software to help drive organic

growth with unique insights, competitor analysis, and unparalleled progress monitoring.

Follow Us on Social Media

We're social and would love to connect! Follow Jessica and Pendragon Consulting on:

Facebook:
https://www.facebook.com/PendragonConsultingLLC

Instagram:
https://www.instagram.com/pendragonconsultingllc/

LinkedIn:
https://www.linkedin.com/company/pendragon-consulting-llc

Twitter:
https://twitter.com/LlcPendragon

Bonus Content

We've put together a few extra tidbits to help you along your journey.

Enjoy!

107 Types of Content for Your Content Marketing Calendar

Content comes in countless forms and is powerful. Expand your efforts with these 100 different types of content you can fill up your content marketing calendar with to build relationships and delight your audience.

1. About Us
2. Apps
3. Ask Me Anything
4. Audiobook
5. Augmented Reality
6. Awards
7. Behind the Scenes
8. Blog Post
9. Breaking News
10. Brochures and Fliers
11. Calendar
12. Case Study
13. Cause
14. Certification Program
15. Challenge
16. Cheat Sheet

17. Checklist
18. Clickbait
19. Collaborative/Co-Branded
20. Comic
21. Company Culture
22. Company News
23. Company Profile
24. Comparison
25. Content
26. Content Library/Resource Section
27. Course
28. Curated Content
29. Current Affairs News
30. Data Analysis
31. Day in the Life
32. Demo/Product Tour
33. Diagram
34. Dictionary
35. Easter Egg
36. Ebook
37. Email
38. Emails
39. Explainer
40. Fact Check
41. Facts
42. Failures (great learning tools!)
43. FAQs
44. Forums
45. Game

46. Gated/Members Only
47. GIFs
48. Goals
49. Gossip (as a starting point for a conversation)
50. Guest Post
51. Guide
52. How-To
53. Human Interest (think inspiration!)
54. Humor
55. In Person Events
56. Industry News
57. Infographic
58. Interview/Q&A
59. Investigative
60. Journalism
61. Landing Page
62. Listicle
63. Lists
64. Live-Streaming Video
65. Magazine
66. Maps
67. Memes
68. Microsites
69. Newsletter
70. Opinion
71. Opposing Perspectives
72. Original Photographs
73. PDF
74. Personal Narrative

75. Personal Profile
76. Photo Gallery
77. Pitch Decks
78. Plugin
79. Podcast
80. Poll
81. Posters
82. Predictions
83. Presentation
84. Press Release
85. Product Reviews
86. Promotion
87. Quiz/Survey
88. Quotes
89. Research Report
90. Roundups of Information
91. Screenshots
92. Search Engine Optimization (SEO)
93. Services
94. Social Media
95. Sponsorships
96. Statistics
97. Stock Images
98. Successes
99. Templates and Worksheets
100. Testimonials
101. Tools (i.e. financial calculators, etc.)
102. Videos
103. Virtual Events

Great Blog Sites

If you're still slightly confused on formatting for blogs, we're including links to some of our favorite marketing and sales blogs for you to check out in alphabetical order.

HubSpot
https://blog.hubspot.com/marketing

Neil Patel
https://neilpatel.com/blog/

Pendragon Consulting, LLC
https://www.pendragonconsultingllc.com/blog

Precision Legal Marketing
https://precisionlegalmarketing.com/law-firm-marketing-blogs/

SalesGig
https://www.salesgig.com/blog

Search Engine Journal
https://www.searchenginejournal.com/

ZoomInfo
https://blog.zoominfo.com/

Social Posts We Love

We've put together a collection of social media posts that we absolutely LOVE and inspire us. We hope they'll inspire you as well!

Check out these posts from Hagemann Wealth Management. The founder, Kurt Hagemann, and his family have a bulldog named Frank that serves as their company mascot. Frank, along with their two other dogs,

Zeus and Ollie, are also featured on their website. Super cute. They've turned their love of their dogs (and the community's love for their dogs) into a marketing tool to drive engagement on social media.

The graphics are all a blend of Frank - a family pet, company mascot and beloved community member - coupled with some awesome wealth management tips. They've turned it into Frank's Corner and Financial Friday. (Frank's graphics post on Friday.)

It all started on National Puppy Day when Frank made his debut. Have a look:

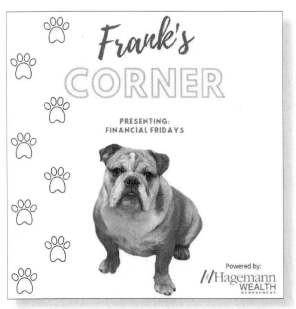

And each week, Frank offers up a new tip in adorable and fun-loving ways.

We also really love the posts that a company called SalesGig offers up. SalesGig is a lead generation marketplace that caters to the B2B world. They have a clear understanding of who their target audience is, and their posts are shaped around that. While their posts are all creative and effectively target their audience, it is actually their use of hashtags that we are *most* impressed with.

You see, an effective social media (and content marketing) strategy includes researching hashtags that can help your posts reach a wider audience *organically*.

We of course, can't forget the big wigs out there, like SEMrush. They are an excellent example for posting value-driven content. Have a look for yourself:

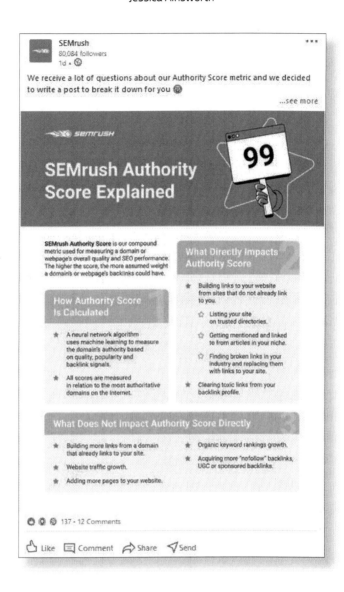

How well does this post fit with our book?! They are an awesome resource!!

We'd be remiss if we didn't include at least one of our own posts in here! To really reach a wider audience on social media, you need to prove that your content is valuable, and that people actually want to see it. The more people that interact (or engage) with your post, the more the social media algorithms will show it. One way we combat that and drive engagement is through the use of National Days a few times a month. It's not enough to attract those outside of our target audience but is enough to boost the engagement rate.

Are you inspired yet?

Infographics

Looking for an example of an infographic? Look no further! We've created some pretty kick butt infographics using Canva, but there are a bunch of different websites you can use to create them.

Free Resources

Check out our own landing page to download your free resources, some of which we've mentioned throughout this book.

Some resources you can expect to find on our website includes:

1. Defining Your Target Audience Worksheet
2. Anatomy of a Blog
3. Blog Checklist
4. Steps to Optimizing Your Facebook Business Page
5. SEO Checklist
6. Infographics
7. And more!

All it costs is your email address. You can unsubscribe from our emails at any time and we do not sell your information. To download your free resources, please visit:

https://www.beginnersguidetomarketing.com/
contentmarketing

About Pendragon Consulting

Your Partner in Expanding the Foregrounds of Digital Marketing Excellence

The story of digital marketing efficacy always starts with an effective strategy. Without a plan, you might as well be aimlessly targeting advertisements that lead to no results.

This is where Pendragon Consulting comes in. A strong penchant for research enables us to create that game plan and give you a strategy that will generate phenomenal results while also improving user engagement.

Who Is Pendragon Consulting?

Results-driven and research-focused, Pendragon Consulting, is a digital marketing agency helping businesses in the service industry gauge and optimize their online presence. We offer our clients a comprehensive range of digital marketing services that encompass our varying expertise.

We understand that your business deserves a stable online presence that delivers results. You put thought into the services you provide and the products you sell; so we put in the effort to make sure your efforts reach the right audience and gain you traction that improves your bottom line.

www.PendragonConsultingLLC.com

hello@pendragonconsultingllc.com

Author Bio

Jessica Ainsworth, Founder of Pendragon Consulting, LLC, a digital marketing agency based out of Maryland, is focused on helping businesses expand their reach into new pools of potential customers. She has a strong background in research and analytics and has turned that into a passion for marketing. Author of *The Beginner's Guide to Facebook Advertising: Create Impactful Ads and Increase Your Return on Investment* and *The Beginner's Guide to Content Marketing: How to Drive Traffic, Provide Value and Increase Revenue*, Jessica loves teaching small businesses how to stand on their own two feet to remain competitive without having to pay an agency to do it for them (unless they want to - in which case, give Pendragon a call).

Former intelligence analyst and total nerd, Jessica has a special fondness for research and analytics. Having a strong background in analytics, marketing seemed like an almost natural career transition. She is a veteran, author, marketing professional, philanthropist and board member at 22 March for Life, a veteran suicide prevention organization.

Connect with Jessica on LinkedIn!

LinkedIn personal: https://www.linkedin.com/in/jessica-ains-3b3194187/

Made in the USA
Columbia, SC
27 November 2020

CHAPTER 10

They met at the stables where Albert had saddled a bay gelding, a good sixteen hands, and a steady horse, just as Victoria had asked for during lunch.

He liked the fact that she could ride, was competent and brave, no simpering miss. That she had requested when her mama was busy ordering a cup of tea by a maid that she did not wish to ride side-saddle, but astride, even more so.

Albert swallowed a curse, having thought himself prepared to see her dressed so. He was not. He shut his mouth with a snap, but could not avert his eyes as he should. The feminine figure on display, the long lean legs made a part of his brain think of the sexual positions book he'd been studying. He had never known a lady, a daughter of a duke to be so bold. She was marvelous.

He bowed, biting back his grin of appreciation. "My lady. Your mighty steed awaits you."

She sauntered past him, and he turned to view her as she went by. What was a man to do when a woman dressed in breeches? He could not help but appreciate the roundness of her curves.

Victoria did not use a mounting block. Instead, she reached up to hold the reins and saddle, lifting her foot high enough to enter the stirrup to pull herself up.

It was an impressive mount that even he sometimes found hard to manage. "Shall we be off?" he asked her, gaining his own seat.

"Where are we going? Is there anywhere particular on the estate you wish to show me?" she asked him, her snug riding jacket and the white shirt beneath accentuating her figure. She looked simply perfect, and his stomach clenched with nerves at having her alone for an hour or so.

"There are several fields that give a good prospect over the house and hedge groves if you wish to jump."

"I would enjoy that, thank you," she said to him, all politeness.

Albert led the way out of the yard, heading up toward the western side of the property and the highest points on his land. They rode in silence for a time, not because they were lost in their own thoughts, he at least, but because he could not make his tongue form the right words to say anything to Victoria.

He sighed, hating that he was unable to voice all that he wanted to her.

"Now that we're to be here for some weeks, I hope that you will let me continue our lessons on gaining you a suitable wife. A woman who will inspire sweet sonnets from your hands." She cast him a curious look. "Do you write at all, my lord? A way to a woman's heart is sometimes through the written word."

He glanced at her, knowing he could write several sonnets, sweet notes, and pages-long letters to Victoria if only she would let him. Words that would sweep her off her delicate feet.

"I do enjoy writing and reading. Are you a reader, Victoria?" he asked, wanting to move the subject away from him.

A small, knowing smile lifted her lips as she looked ahead. "I love to read. Gothic romances are my favorite."

At the mention of the genre that he wrote, Albert schooled his features lest she think he'd swallowed his own tongue.

"Any in particular?" Albert prayed she hadn't read his novels. The thought of the woman he wanted to be his wife having read his work sent a whole new set of emotions roiling through him. Fear, pride, but most of all the concern that she hated his books. Dear God, what if she loathed the author him. However, would he move forward with their plan knowing all the while that she hated his books? They were like extensions of him—his book children.

"I adore all the works by Elbert Retsek, but especially the third book in his Beuroguard series. The captain is swoon-worthy while also being quite the scary, forceful character. I would love to meet Mr. Retsek one day, but I doubt I ever will. What with him being such a recluse and wishing to remain anonymous."

Albert listened to her and fought not to crow. She liked his books. Lady Victoria Worthingham was an enthusiast of his work. Such truths were worthy of a few whoops, and arm waving. Instead, Albert smiled, agreeing with her whole-heartedly.

"I enjoy Mr. Retsek's work also," he admitted. As the Mr. Retsek, how could he not agree with Victoria's claim? It pleased him she enjoyed his writing. He strove to make each book better, more action-filled, suspenseful, and darker than the last, so to hear a reader say his books were some of their favorites warmed his soul.

"If only he would come out of the darkness and into the light. Share the joy he gives his readers and relish the acco-

63

lades that he is worthy of. Do you not think?" she asked him, watching him keenly.

Albert wished he could step into the light as she said, but he knew he could not. It took all his consideration and effort merely to keep a conversation going with Victoria. The idea of going into a bookstore, of talking to readers, and God forbid, reading aloud from his words sent a shiver of horror down his spine. He was incapable of such an act.

"Maybe one day he will. We will both have to live in hope." As much as such a thought scared him, he wished he could be more outgoing and easy about people. He wasn't sure why he was the way he was, but he had to think some of his troubles stemmed from his father's bullying to both him and his mama. His father's death had been a blessing in the end. His years of verbal abuse had ended when he'd breathed his last breath.

"We shall have to, I agree."

Victoria was quiet a moment as they walked up toward the top of a hill that gave a great prospective of the house. "Do you think, should the opportunity arise, that you could ride in Hyde Park with a lady of your choice? Your conversation with me seems very easy. I think that if you relaxed, you could be just so with someone else."

Not that he wanted to be so with anyone other than the lady he was riding with right now. How to make her see him as a potential suitor when he found the words so hard to say. He supposed he could always write her a sonnet. A love letter...

"I would find it difficult, especially if she showed little interest in what I had to say or found my company boring. And anyway," he said, remembering her words from yesterday's lesson. "I thought love notes were frowned upon in society?"

"Society does not need to know everything." She wiggled

her brows before taking in his lands with pleasure. "And you are not at all boring, Albert," she declared, sending him a scolding look. "Any lady would be overjoyed to have your affections."

You are not one of them, he wanted to add to his chagrin.

He doubted that many women even knew of his existence, marquess or not. "That is because you are my friend. I have known you for as long as I've known your brother. You are easy to speak with, and I like you more than most."

She chuckled, and he enjoyed the sound of her giggle. He wished to hear it more often. "You would do marvelous, I'm sure, given a little moral support, and that is what I'm here for. There is to be a country dance at Camberley and a ball at Lord Hammilyn's. We are attending both, and I hope to hear you will also. It is a ball in your county, after all. It would be rude not to attend."

He knew of the country dance at Camberley she spoke of. It was the very one each year he was invited to and never attended. Although he ensured the finest musicians came up from London to play for his neighbors and nearby towns-folk. "How could I refuse with you being there by my side." And maybe, if he could bring forth some dutch courage, he could ask her for another waltz and start his courting of a woman in earnest. Not just any suitable miss, but Lady Victoria Worthingham.

CHAPTER 11

*V*ictoria stopped at the top of the hill and overlooked Lord Melvin's estate. The property was very pretty, almost as pretty as Dunsleigh, and she could see herself very happily situated in such a place.

Her deceased husband's estate had been near Blackpool in northwest England. The home had been adequate and large, well kept, but the landscape had been so very different to Surrey that Victoria knew she would rarely visit there. Hampshire, however, could capture anyone's heart, as it had hers.

The matrimonial road had not been a success for her, but that did not mean that Albert should be so unlucky. She wanted him to have love, friendship, and passion in his life. The ball would allow her to help him choose a couple of suitable ladies and perhaps dance with them. There was no reason for him to be worried about the event. She would not let anything happen to him.

"I shall have the ladies fawning at your feet by the end of the night, Albert. You shall be pleased with the results. I promise you."

His visage looked a little green and unsure, and she wondered why the idea of such an evening made him so uncomfortable. She would seek out Josh and ask if he knew any particulars about his lordship, a little insight into his past that may help her with his future.

"Tell me what other courting particulars you're going to teach me to win a lady's heart."

Victoria thought about his question a moment. "I will impart the need to be confident, my lord. I'm going to speak plainly, as crass as that is, but some things need to be said." She cast a glance over her shoulder and took in account of how far away their groom was. Hopefully, far enough that he would not hear. "You are an attractive gentleman and a marquess. I stand by my promise of having you betrothed before the next Season."

Albert jumped down off his horse, striding to stand under a large oak. Victoria followed him, hoping she had not upset him with her forward words. She could sometimes be a little too presumptuous, bossy even. She did not want to offend.

"I have pushed you a little too much, have I not?" She caught his eye, reaching out to clasp his arm to make him look at her. "Are you angry with me, Lord Melvin?"

He sighed, running a hand through his hair and leaving it on end. The sight of him a little disheveled made her catch her breath. How was it that this man could not already be married? It was impossible to fathom.

"What should I do if the lady, at someplace and time, tries to kiss me?" he asked her.

Relief rolled through her that he wasn't troubled by her help after all, but of the particulars of courtship. "I kissed Mr. Armstrong on the night he proposed." Not that it had been life-altering. If anything, it had been awfully fast and very wet. A shiver of revulsion ran down her spine at the memory of it. "But before that I did not. It is not what is done." She chewed her lip in thought. "I will tell you this, my lord. My sisters had disclosed that they all kissed their husbands before they were married and say it is most enlightening and pleasant. I should think you may steal a kiss or two if you're set on marrying the one particular lady."

His lips thinned into a displeased line. "Your husband kissed you?"

She blinked, unsure where the conversation was headed. "Of course. I was married to him for six weeks before he hied off with his lover."

"He ought to die a thousand deaths for hurting you so. If I had you to kiss every night, no one could drag me from your side."

The breath in her lungs whooshed out at his words. Had Albert's voice dipped an octave or two, and why did the sound of his voice, his words make her feel odd and achy. "That is a very sweet thing to say."

He stared down at her, a dark and hungry light in his eyes that she was unsure the meaning of. "I have never kissed anyone. Pitiful, am I not?"

"Would you like me to be your first kiss, Albert? To practice on me before another lady, one whom you wish to marry, steps before you?" she added as an afterthought, reminding him she was the teacher here, nothing else.

"I would not presume that you would be a willing participant to my kisses." He stepped closer, and the heat of his body warmed her.

She raised her brow, wishing he had not said that. "I'm never marrying again, my lord. My situation in life, fortunately, does not state that I have to. But I would like to kiss you, no matter what you may think. You are my friend and I'm here to help. If you wished to kiss me, I would not refuse you."

The thought of kissing the handsome man towering over

her was enticing. "Tell the groom to turn about and kiss me, Lord Melvin."

"John," he called. "Please, turn about for a moment."

The groom did as Albert asked without question.

She watched, transfixed as Albert seemed to will the courage through himself to kiss her. Victoria could feel herself shaking. Oddly she was a little nervous about kissing him. Once engaged, her husband-to-be had kissed her often. Never had she felt the bubbling up of expectation as she did right now. There was something different about the man standing before her, gaining his nerve that her husband never had.

You want to kiss Albert. The thought of kissing Paul was never exciting.

He wrapped his arm around her waist, pulling her against him. She gasped, having not expected him to be so bold. "Last chance, Lady Victoria," he said, dipping his head.

Victoria could feel herself leaning into him, willing his lips to touch hers. Heat coursed through her veins like fire at their first touch. His tentative lips urged and beckoned her to kiss him. It was neither wet nor fast, simply a slow seduction that spiraled her wits to the wind.

She wrapped her arms about his neck, touching the silky hair on his nape, liking the feel of it slipping through her fingers. His hands flexed, clutching tighter against her back, and the pit of her stomach clenched with need. A familiar ache that she recognized as desire. On the few occasions Paul had lain with her after their marriage, his bedding was thankfully much more skilled than his kissing.

Albert deepened the kiss, his tongue tangling with hers. Victoria flung herself into the embrace, wanting more kisses if this was how they were supposed to be. Wicked and delicious. Any wonder her sisters looked flushed and wistful around their husbands.

He moaned, reaching up to cradle her face, and the kiss changed. No longer slow and coaxing, but deep and demanding. Victoria kissed him with everything she had, reveling in the feel of him, his labored breaths, his arduous need. His hand splayed into her hair, sending multiple pins to scatter to the earth beneath their feet.

She cared naught for all of it. All she could think about was his kiss, their first kiss. How wonderful that she could have her first real, passionate kiss with a friend, a man she admired and cared for above anyone else. She closed the space between them, her breasts, her nipples, hard little peaks under her shirt and riding jacket. The feel of his chest teased and taunted, but she could not stop. She wanted more. So much more than kissing, and that in itself ought to give her pause, but it did not.

*A*lbert could not get enough of Victoria. Hell, he'd wanted to kiss her almost from the very first moment he'd met her, and that was several years ago when he was still in short coats at Eton.

The woman in his arms, slender and yet womanly, tall and yet short enough that he had to lean down a little to kiss her. Long, soft strawberry-blonde hair was silky between his fingers. Her skin soft, her mouth pliant and willing and right at this moment, driving him to the point of madness.

He'd never kissed a woman before, hadn't known what to do when she suggested that she be his first. Would she think less of him if she knew all of his secrets? That he'd not only never kissed a woman but had never slept with one either. From watching the few friends he had over the years when they married, their wives were always quite satisfied with their husband's talents.

He would have none of the roguish experience that they

did. Of course, he knew the particulars. He had read extensively after all, but doing the sexual act was another beast entirely.

But now, kissing Victoria, something told him that it wasn't something to fear, but long for. Her hands, clutching his hair, her breathy moans when he teased her soft lips with little nibbles and short kisses drove him to the point of madness.

Had he been a rake, a man of the world, he would know how to seduce her, bring them both to a pleasurable conclusion. With her a widow, such an interlude could be a possibility. But he did not know how to do any of those things or even how to go about starting such progress.

Albert kissed her hard, forcing his hands to remain on her hips when she surged against his hard cock. Stars burst behind his eyes, and he went to distance themselves. Victoria made a noise of annoyance, holding him firmly in place.

"Do not deny me," she said between kisses.

Albert forgot all thoughts of where they were. The fact that her brother the duke could too be out riding the grounds and could find them entangled. That the groom was merely a few feet from them. All forgotten at her whispered words.

The kiss turned savage. His body aflame with need, his cock so hard that he was certain he would come should she continue what she was doing.

They needed to stop. One of them needed to end this madness before they tumbled to the ground, and he fumbled his way into having her at the top of a hill with nothing but grass at her back.

He broke the kiss. "We need to end this. Now. Before it is too late."

She stared at him, her eyes wide and glassy with desire. She blinked several times before they cleared, and the woman in his arms was once again the sensible, intelligent Victoria he'd always known.

"Of course, yes," she breathed, stepping away. She checked her riding breeches and jacket before reaching up and pinning her hair back to rights. "Well, that was certainly a very good lesson, do you not think?"

Frustration shot through him that after such a kiss, a soul-shattering one such as the one they shared, that it would be termed a lesson. He stood mute for a moment, unable to form the words to reply.

"We should probably return to Rosedale." Victoria walked over to her horse and gained her seat without help.

Albert shook himself free of the melancholy that threatened his good mood and mounted too. "We shall go this way, it is a shorter way back, but the view is just as good as the one here on the hilltop."

She nodded, turning her horse and starting down the hill. Albert spun around in his saddle and noticed the groom waiting discreetly behind them, no sign on his visage that he judged them over what they had just done.

Which, by the looks of Victoria, was nothing at all. How on earth was he supposed to court her, even if she were not aware of such things, if she was so adamant that marriage was not an option she wished to consider.

He didn't want any other lady whom she would train him to woo. He wanted her, yet even he knew that she would not be an easy woman to win. She would take all his effort, his patience, and the wooing skills he possessed.

Which, unfortunately, were not many.

He kicked his mount on, following close behind Victoria as they snaked their way down the hill back to Rosedale. His mind a whirr of thoughts on how to win a lady who did not want to be won.

CHAPTER 12

*V*ictoria lay in bed later that night, staring at the ornate painting on the ceiling. She had left her curtains open this balmy evening on some of her windows, allowing the cooling breeze off the lake to enter her room.

Her mind would not settle, and it was no wonder after the kiss she shared with Albert earlier that day. She had not particularly known how to act after it and so had dismissed the kiss as a good first attempt at teaching him to be a rake.

She'd never kissed a gentleman like that before, not even her husband while he was bedding her. Could they be soft and slow, a seduction of the senses? Or deep and demanding, taking her breath away and leaving her witless such as the one they shared? Paul's kisses had been awful, nothing like Albert's.

Victoria sighed. Albert had kissed her as if she were precious, as if he wanted to kiss her, not for teaching purposes, but because he wanted *her*.

She thumped the bed with her hands, hating that she did not know which one it was for Albert. Not that she should be mulling over their interlude at all, she reminded herself. She wasn't marrying Albert or any gentleman. The kiss was nothing special, and she was being a fool giving herself ideas that it was for Albert at least.

At this rate she was never going to fall to sleep. Throwing back the bedding, she reached for her dressing gown at the end of her bed and started for the door. A nice, hot cup of milk would do her. She could always ring a maid, but the house had been abed for hours now, and it would not be fair to wake everyone just because she could not sleep.

Victoria checked the hall, and not seeing anyone about, used her candle to make her way to the servant's stairs, knowing these stairs would come out directly across from the kitchens.

This time of night, she encountered no one about. The oven illuminated the kitchen, its bright, burning coals giving her light. She placed her candle on the long, wooden table and turned to the large dresser, finding the milk covered with a cloth to keep out any bugs.

She poured some into the pot, enough for a cup, and placed it on the top of the stove. A stool sat close by, and Victoria sat down, waiting for her milk to warm.

"I did not think a duke's daughter would know her way around the kitchen."

The male voice, familiar and welcome as the cup of milk encircled her, and Victoria stood, pushing down her absurd, enthusiastic reaction to Albert's appearance at the door.

That he was dressed in tan breeches and a shirt, his cravat untied and hanging loosely about his neck, only made him appear more handsome than she needed to think him.

He was not for her. No man was, never again would she be played a fool by a gentleman. Paul had cured her of any ideas of marriage after his treatment of her. She was an heiress, a widow who could direct her own life, go and do whatever she pleased whenever it pleased her. She did not need a husband tagging along, or worse, telling her she could not go or do such things.

But, oh dear, he did look very handsome, all disheveled and rumpled. His hair appeared like he had run his hand through it several times since she saw him at dinner. Was he also thinking of the kiss, of what a mistake it may have been to tumble over?

Victoria calmed her worries, determined to be as confident and professional as she possibly could around him. He was her friend. They had an agreement. She would help him gain a wife, he would tell her he was the author, Elbert Retsek, marry another and she would go home with her mama and start her widowhood in earnest.

"I could not sleep and hoped a glass of milk might help me. Would you like one?" she offered.

He pulled up a chair and sat across from her. "No, thank you. I heard a noise on my way to bed and thought to come and investigate. I'm glad that we're alone. I want to talk to you about the kiss this afternoon."

Victoria willed the heat to dissipate from her cheeks at the mention of their embrace. She blamed it on the fire in the hearth instead. "There is no need to discuss the kiss, my lord. It was merely an instruction between friends on how you would kiss a wife. I will admit you did a very fine job of."

He cleared his throat, his eyes going wide. Had she shocked him yet again? She was known in her family always to speak her mind, to have opinions that not everyone wished to hear all of the time, and yet, such disapproval never deterred her. She simply persisted with her ways.

"I hope that our kiss has not discouraged you from helping me gain a wife. I would still like your help if you're willing to continue."

Relief poured through her like a balm. "Of course I'm willing to help still. In fact, we can pick up the lessons after breakfast if you would like. Perhaps we could meet in the music room. There is a pianoforte in there, and I would like to give you instruction on what to say and how to act when your particular young lady takes a seat to play for an audience."

His head cocked thoughtfully, and she hoped they could move forward from today. They were friends, after all. Surely male and female fellows could remain so, even after sharing such an intimate act.

"That would be most helpful."

The milk on the stove started to boil, and Albert stood, picking up a nearby mitten before clasping the pot. He poured the milk into her mug with care, not a drop spilled.

"Would you like sugar in your milk?" he asked her, placing the pot in the sink.

"No, thank you. The milk will be enough." She sipped her drink, watching him. "You are sure that you wish to take a wife, Albert? I do not want to force these lessons on you if you're not ready to settle down."

He sat again across from her, folding his hands in his lap, his legs a little parted in his ease of seating. "I am ready to marry. Out here in Hampshire, there isn't much to do most of the year, and the company would be nice. I also long for children to make the house sing with giggles and squeals. I cannot wait for those days to come."

Victoria found herself entranced by his words, his ideals. His future sounded so very pleasant, and once, maybe, there was a time she too wanted such things. Her first days of marriage had been lovely, but it wasn't long before disillusionment creeped into her world. The whispers of Paul and where he spent his nights, the spending, the not seeing him for days on end. Never again would she be a man's property, uncared for and treated like rubbish. Now she wished for adventure—independence above all things, a life of her own on her own.

"I hope you get your wish and with my help, maybe sooner rather than later. I may not teach you everything you need to know to gain a wife. Some things like today's kiss should never happen again. But most etiquette and proper conversation skills I can help with. And my connections, of course, while we're staying here with you in Hampshire, will help draw suitable ladies to your side."

He reached out, picking up her hand. He did not wear gloves, and her attention shifted to his arms, his rolled-up shirtsleeves that gave her an advantageous view of his muscled arms. His fingers were long and warm, strong, and she shivered, remembering what they felt like against her back, holding her firmly upon his chest.

His eyes met hers, and as if in slow motion, his mouth lowered to her hand and kissed her fingers. She sucked in a breath, feeling his lips, the touch of his mouth against her flesh as if he had kissed her a second time on the lips. Her nipples beaded, and she became aware of how little she was wearing.

Oh dear Lord, what was happening to her? She could not react to this man. Albert was her friend, possibly her favorite author in all the world. She could not lust after him.

That would never do at all.

"I must go," she said, wrenching out of his hold and fleeing the room. "Goodnight," she said at the door, not waiting to hear his reply. Lord Melvin was starting to be a danger, and she needed to calm herself before she saw him again. His reply, husky and low, made longing rip through her. Damn it all, this plan of hers may have been a bad one after all, and she never had bad ideas. Ever.

CHAPTER 13

*A*s agreed, they met in the music room the following morning. Albert walked into the chamber and steeled himself for spending some time with Victoria.

Alone.

She was the epitome of perfection. She stood gracefully beside an open window, the sheer curtains floating past the bottom of her dress, her hair up in curls, several loose and bouncing against her slim shoulder. As for her gown, it fell against her form in the most flattering of ways, revealing her luscious curves and bountiful breasts.

Albert should look away, should not be torturing himself with designs on a woman who did not want a husband, but he could not help himself. She was all that he wanted. He would play her game of instruction if only to win her heart with seduction if need be.

He cleared his throat, and she turned, the pensive, thoughtful expression immediately replaced with one of welcome, her smile warming the room even more than it already was.

"Good morning, Lady Victoria. I hope you slept well."

She nodded once, starting for the pianoforte where she sat on the leather stool. "I did, thank you. I hope you're ready for your next lesson?"

He joined her, leaning over the pianoforte and one that had been in his family since he could remember. "What is it you wish to instruct me on today?"

"Well, as to that. I wanted to talk to you about what you could do to offer help, show interest when the lady you are courting is taking part in a musical night or an impromptu concert after dinner."

Albert knew already what he should do. He knew everything if he were truthful. It was only with Victoria could he be relaxed enough to do what he ought as a gentleman. There was something about her that his soul found comforting, enough to stop his spluttering or his inability to speak at all. Women made him anxious, all but Victoria. She made him nervous. There was a large difference between the two.

"If your lady is called to play a song, you may escort her to the pianoforte, offer to help her with her music while she plays. If you're able, you may even offer to sing a duet with her."

All reasonable suggestions, not that he'd ever been able to do such things. During his first season, he tried to act the part of a marquess searching for a wife, being all gentlemanly and correct. He had offered to turn the music pages, had bumbled the page turn, and the music had ended on top of the lady's hands before falling to the floor.

He had stopped trying to play the part of an able-bodied lord after that.

Until Victoria, that was.

"Let us play a little game. I shall stay here and choose music to play—a duet. You shall come and offer assistance and sing with me. Let us practice to make you perfect when such an opportunity arises for you."

"Very well." Albert walked away and waited for Victoria to settle herself at the pianoforte. Her music set out before her. He came back over to her, bowing. "May I turn the pages for you, Lady Victoria?" he asked her, his body clenching at the sight of her biting her bottom lip, playing a coy miss, not having expected a lord to ask to help her.

"Thank you, Lord Melvin. That is most kind." She looked up at him from under her eyelashes, and he could almost imagine this was real, that he was so suave and capable of pulling off such a triumph.

"Not at all. You play so wonderfully. It is an honor to help."

She dipped her head, but not before he saw the small grin on her lips.

Victoria started to play *For Tenderness Form'd in Life's Early Days*, the music flowing from her fingers as if the pianoforte were a part of her body, fluid and perfect with each keystroke. For a time, Albert lost himself in the music before her voice broke into song, and he knew what it was to hear perfection.

He joined her, his deeper baritone melding perfectly with her higher octave. His eyes met hers, and he read her surprise, having not known that he could sing. He could do many things. Just his inability to do them well when about the company of others was his issue.

Her lips broke out into a smile as their voices blended to a harmonious, delightful sound. He was thankful that he could sing, for it was days such as this one that he would forever cherish. Being here with Victoria, enjoying her company, turning the pages, and singing with her as if he were the epitome of gentlemanly behavior and breeding made bearing this rogue tutoring worthwhile.

In the book he was penning, he would include a scene like this one, mayhap have the villain in the story come in and ruin the harmonious playing and singing between two lovers.

Would Victoria guess when she read the novel that it was based on this very day? He had never wanted to be prominent. The idea made him physically ill, thinking about meeting all the people who longed to do so. But would it be so bad if one woman knew who his pseudonym was?

The song came to an end, and with the turning of the last page, Albert could not tear his eyes from Victoria. Her eyes held his, luminous and large. Her lips slightly apart as if she could not quite fathom how in sync they had been.

"You sing beautifully, Albert." Her fingers slid off the ebony keys, settling in her lap.

He wanted to tell her that while he may sing in such a way, she was the one who was beautiful in all ways. A woman after his own heart. Hell, what was he thinking? After his heart? She had captured it a long time ago. If only he could capture hers.

"My singing is nothing compared to yours, and your playing. You are proficient at the pianoforte."

She stood, placing herself closer to him. Albert did not move, merely stared down at her. His stomach clenched, heat swirling in his gut. He wanted to kiss her again. Hell, he wanted to do a lot more than that, even if his virgin body did not know entirely what *that* involved.

Her attention dipped to his lips, and she leaned closer still. She was but a breath from him. Did she want him to kiss her again? He wished he was a rogue and able to make a choice, take what he wanted, but the small voice of uncertainty whispered against his ear, stopping him from taking her lips again.

"How wonderful that you played so well together." The sound of the Duchess of Penworth's voice at the music room door wrenched all thoughts of kissing Victoria away. Albert stepped back, bowing, while disappointment stabbed at him at a lost opportunity.

"Good morning, Your Grace. I did not know you were listening."

She smiled, but her eyes flicked to her daughter. Victoria stood silent, but a blush kissed her cheeks.

"I did not think you knew I was here." The duchess smiled. "Would you accompany me upstairs, daughter? I wish for you to help me pick a gown for our drive about Hampshire tomorrow. I assume we're still going to have the picnic."

"Of course," Albert said, remembering he'd offered to take them on a picnic at dinner the night before. "It does not look like it will storm any time soon. The picnic will be possible, I'm sure."

"Verry good. Victoria?" the duchess said again, pinning her daughter with a *follow me* look.

Albert watched them go, uncertain if the duchess had seen all that had transpired after their duet. She must have, or at least said she had heard the music but had intervened when she noticed their closeness.

Damn it, he did not want to get Victoria into a dispute, nor did he want them to leave early due to his carelessness.

He was so untutored in being a rake he did not even remember or think to close the music room door when they had entered.

Idiot.

*V*ictoria closed the door to her mother's bedroom, steeling herself for the coming conversation, which she was sure would have something to do with the near-second-kiss between her and Albert.

Her mother walked over to the window and stared out over the grounds. "Please tell me that I did not almost walk in on you and Lord Melvin kissing just before?" Her mama turned to her, pinning her to the spot.

Victoria winced, wondering if she should lie or tell the truth and admit her mistake. The second one she was just about to make, not the first. Her mama did not need to know everything.

"You know that I am helping his lordship in gaining a wife. I was merely trying to help him navigate around a musical evening, how to woo a lady while helping her play the pianoforte. Be supportive of her as she plays. You caught us close, and I know what it must have looked like. But we were not going to do anything, Mama. Do not be so silly." So, it looked like she was going to lie to her parent. Better that, before they were bundled up in the carriage and returned to Dunsleigh before her instruction on Lord Melvin was complete. Or her finding out the truth of his life.

"If your brother had caught you, he would have demanded that you announce your betrothal. That is how it looked to me. Do not be forward, Victoria. After the dealings we've had settling your sisters, your marriage that I'm sure society will be discussing for years to come, so abominably did Mr. Armstrong behave, I do not think I could withstand another scandal. Please, if you are considering Lord Melvin as a lover, remain above reproach and ensure such trysts cannot be seen or come upon by anyone."

Guilt pricked her conscience, and she went to her mama, clasping her hands. "I promise, Mama I shall not do anything that will put me or the family name at risk. I am a friend of Lord Melvin's, that is all. With friendship comes a little intimacy, I find. I will not be caught in a compromising position." Victoria crossed her fingers behind her back, knowing that she would have to be extra careful after today.

What was worse was that she had done nothing but think

about their shared kiss. Of his lips taking hers. What would happen if they did it again?

The sound of the luncheon gong echoed through the halls, and Victoria reached over and kissed her mama's cheeks. "I shall see you at lunch, Mama."

She fled the room, not entirely convinced her mother believed her words. But she would try, no matter how she responded to Lord Melvin when in his presence, to attempt to tame that part of her that wanted to push him a little. To see if he could be a rake with her as well to his preferred future bride. She would be a liar if she were to declare that a little flirtation with a handsome gentleman wasn't a lovely way to spend a day.

After lunch, she would seek Albert out for further lessons. There was under a fortnight to the country dance, and he wasn't yet ready. But he would be. She would make certain of it, even if she had to use herself as his prop for teaching.

Just as long as her mama never caught them again.

CHAPTER 14

*L*ater that evening, Albert found Victoria alone in the library, a room he allowed guests, when he had them, that was, to use at their own leisure. It was not where he wrote, nor did it hold any identifying manuscripts that guests could see and link to him.

He frowned, thinking of the one page he had misplaced while at Dunsleigh. Had he left it on the desk in the library? The duchess knew that he had used the room. Surely she would know it belonged to him, but would she know what it was that he had left? That he could not say.

He strode into the room, pulling Victoria's consideration from the book she was bent over, a few wisps of her strawberry-blond hair covering her cheek. As he moved closer, he noticed that she not only had hair over her face but was chewing on the end of one curl.

His body hardened at the sight of her lips suckling on the golden lock. Oh dear God, she would kill him before he had a chance to use her instruction against a potential bride.

Not that he wanted anyone but her, but he was still to

work on the particular issue. First, he had to learn to be a rake, and then he could use his skills to win her hand.

"Lady Victoria, what are you reading?"

Her eyes went wide, and she started on the settee, looking past him as if to ensure they were alone. "Shut the door and lock it, Lord Melvin. My mama does not know that I am up, she thought I went to bed an hour ago, but I did not. I snuck in here."

Albert did as she bade, coming back to the chair. "What is it that you're reading?" he asked again, sitting.

She lifted the book, and he felt the blood drain out of his face. She had found the erotic etchings his father had purchased on his grand tour after graduating from university. The very one's he'd been reading for some months. For a moment, he could not speak. Did she think such drawings were his? The idea of such an assumption made his heart stop, and humiliation shriveled it up to a dried prune.

"How wonderful that you have this book. Look, the pictures in it are amazing, and I'm sure should you study them, you may learn the ways of a woman. Become a wonderful lover."

He cleared his throat, stupefied at the image she studied. A man and woman, entwined, but not head to head, it was head to toe, except they were not suckling each other's feet, but their genitals.

He'd seen the book, had looked at it before his first season, and had thought it marvelous, not that he'd had the ability to become rakish as the men in the book depicted.

"It was my father's. He's had it since he was a young man."

"What do you think they're doing here?" she asked, turning the book this way and that.

"Having sex without intercourse," he said bluntly. She looked at him, the light in her eyes curious, and he willed himself not to ask her if she'd like to do such things with

86

him. Had she never experimented with her husband? Possibly not, since the fool found comfort in everyone else's bed except his wife.

Damn, he would adore to have her so.

He ought to study the book more and learn the way of a woman's body and know what to do with his mouth and cock when the time came. The idea of leaving a woman unsatisfied was almost as bad as not knowing his own name.

She turned the page, and the image made her gasp, a sweet sound that went directly to his throbbing cock. The man, this time, was going down on a woman, her legs spread wide, her face contorted into a vision of pleasure. Her arms clenching the bedding, maddening even to look at visually.

"Well, I say," she whispered, shifting a little on the settee. "What do you think the woman gets out of such interactions with her lover?"

Albert had taken himself in hand, knew pleasure, even if he had never found it with a woman. "She would climax from his kiss there. He would suckle and kiss her with his lips and tongue, bring her to a peak of pleasure that is one of life's greatest gifts."

"Married as I was, I still did not know any of this was possible." She stared at him, her tongue darting out to lick her lips. "Have you ever found such gratification in this way with a woman?"

He closed his eyes, willing himself for strength. "No."

She narrowed her eyes. "With yourself then?"

He nodded, unsure how much he should tell her. The conversation was already scandalous, and should her brother even hear of them speaking so, widow or not, they would be before a priest before the crack of dawn.

Which, in Albert's opinion, would not be so bad. As for Victoria, she would feel managed, pressured, and would hate him for it. If she were to marry him, it had to be of her own fruition.

"Yes, it's possible for both men and women."

Her gasp of breath was just audible, and his stomach clenched, the need to taste her lips, suckle her mouth as much as he wanted to do such things to other parts of her body burned through him. As a man, surely it would not be so difficult to learn how to seduce a woman. He was comfortable with Victoria, hell, they had already shared a kiss, and that seemed as natural as breathing.

He wanted more of the same. But how to make her see that he was more than just a friend one could be honest and open with. The man for her, if only she would see him.

Victoria turned her attention back to the book, flipping the page over to a new drawing. Albert swallowed hard. The image was of a woman, on her knees and hands, the man thrusting into her from behind.

Again the woman's face was contorted into one of pleasure, the man's also, showing enjoyment.

"You cannot tell me that this is a position that a couple would partake in." Victoria studied the image, turning the book this way and that. "I do not think this would feel very enjoyable."

She was literally killing him. As a man who had never laid with a woman, to want one as much as he wanted Victoria and have her speak of sex, studying images of the act was torture.

His cock was erect, weeping, and damn it, he wanted her to touch him. He wanted to bend her over the settee where they now sat and take her in such a way until they both found release.

"From what I understand, that act is possible and enjoyable for both."

She glanced up at him, her eyes widened. "You speak as if

you are unsure." She stared at him, her eyes narrowing. "Are you a virgin, Albert?"

Should he tell her the truth? Something told him that Victoria held the truth in high regard, and it would do him little favor if he were to lie to her. And there was no shame in being a virgin. If anything, he ought to pride himself on the fact that he hadn't squirted his seed all over London with abandonment.

"I am indeed a virgin. Does that shock you?"

She bit her lip yet again, and his attention snapped to her lips. They were so close on the settee he could feel the heat of her body, the sweet, flowery scent of her hair. He wanted to run his fingers through it. Hell, he wanted to do a lot of things. Kiss her soft, supple skin along her back while he took her just as the image before them depicted.

"No," she said, shaking her head. "I like it that you are."

Albert leaned forward, needing to taste her, wanting her with a need that surpassed the nervousness that usually accompanied him whenever he spoke to a woman. With Victoria, conversation, silence, everything was easier, and he wanted to kiss her again. Had since the moment their last one ended.

CHAPTER 15

$\mathcal{V}$ ictoria wrenched herself out of the chair. The tome depicting numerous sexual positions thumped onto the Aubusson rug. She stepped back from both Albert and the book, needing space.

"I should probably return to my room. I shall see you at breakfast. Goodnight Albert."

He looked up at her with such longing, such need that her stomach fluttered and clenched with delicious expectation. When they had been discussing the book, her body had not been itself. A maddening thrum between her legs tortured her, a longing she'd never felt with Paul.

Strange ideas of him kissing her at the apex of her thighs, of holding his dark locks in her hands as he pleasured her would not abate.

He stood and bowed. "Goodnight, my lady." He bent down and picked up the book, always the gentleman. Not pushing her for what they both desired. And God help her, she wanted him to kiss her again. A fact that was utterly perplexing since she was determined to remain alone for the remainder of her life. Enjoy her inheritance, her widowhood, travel, and live.

But what is life without pleasure? a little voice teased.

She dipped into a quick curtsy and fled the room. Albert had said that a woman could give herself pleasure. Was he correct? Paul had never stated as much to her, but then when it came to her late husband, he often kept her in the dark.

Victoria could not make her room fast enough, and she locked the door to ensure privacy. What did he mean by that statement? She had never found much interest in herself before, not in that way at least.

She pulled the bedding back and climbed under the sheets, lying and staring up at the darkened ceiling. More research was needed on the subject before she could determine if that were true.

The following morning Victoria ordered a bath and sent her maid downstairs to press her morning gown for a second time. She locked the door and asked not to be disturbed, determined to learn her body more before she confronted Albert of his claim.

She slipped into the bath, sighing at that feel of the warm, fragrant water. Finding the cake of soap, Victoria washed, running it over her beasts. They were large, and she couldn't quite fit one in each hand. Men normally did take in her bust size, but she had always ignored the admiring glances. That was until Albert looked at her. What was it about the man that made her body question all her choices? Her plans for her future.

Her thumb and forefinger slid over her nipples. They peaked under the water, and she squeezed a little, imaging Albert's hand touching her so. Heat licked between her legs, and she lay her head back, closing her eyes.

For all his awkwardness, there had been none present last evening in the library. If she did not know him so very well, she would have imagined him a rake, seeking to seduce.

She slipped one hand over her flat stomach, soothing the need that thrummed between her legs. The thatch of curls tickled her fingers, and she touched herself there. But what was she supposed to do now?

Victoria frowned, placing her hands on the edge of the bath and tapping her fingers along its side. Annoyance ran through her that she felt as though she needed to do something, but what? All her interactions with Paul had been quick and in the dark. A lot of panting, on his behalf, a groan or two and then it was over. He certainly never fondled her with his hands or his mouth as the drawing she'd seen depicted.

Finishing her bath, she stood and dried herself, letting her maid back in to help her dress. She slid on the light muslin gown of mauve before starting downstairs, determined to find Lord Melvin and discuss this pleasure one could have without a bedpartner.

If she were to remain unmarried for the rest of her days, having satisfaction would be a boon she had to have.

*A*lbert heard the determined strides of Victoria long before he caught sight of her. His heart stuttered at the vision she made, her mauve gown accentuating her delectable form, just made for petting and kissing. Her voluptuous bust that he wanted for himself, to suckle and feast upon.

How could she want to remain unmarried when he could make her life fulfilling and enjoyable if only she would allow herself to fall in love? Place her trust in another, but this time, a genuine gentleman such as he.

He was working in a small room at the back of the house that guests normally overlooked. It had used to be his mother's sewing room due to the large windows, but he had now taken it over as a smoking room, although he never partook in such activities. Preferring to sit and read or plot his books when the muse struck.

As it had this morning after last night with Victoria in the library. His next release would be much steamier than his last, and no doubt get the ladies' hearts fluttering and the men's cravats too tight.

"Here you are. I have been looking all over for you."

He smiled up at her, gesturing for her to sit. "Good morning, Victoria. I hope you slept well."

She closed the door, the snip of the lock loud in the room. His body tensed at the determination written across her features.

"No, I did not. I need to know what this pleasure is you speak of that a woman can find. I know this is utterly inappropriate, but nothing that I tried this morning brought me any such thing. Paul certainly did not arouse me in such a way so the idea of bringing oneself to satisfaction is questionable. You must show me what you mean."

Albert choked on the tea he had been sipping. He coughed, bending forward to try to gain his breath and his senses.

"You want me to what?" he wheezed, trying to clear his lungs of his beverage.

"You need to show me pleasure that I can perform myself. I'm certain I'm doing something wrong."

He felt his mouth grow slack while his cock tightened. "You know that I cannot do that."

"I know no such thing," she said, raising a defiant brow. "I want you to touch me and show me. I'm not a virgin nor a debutante taking her first turn, need I remind you. I'm quite determined."

And frustrated if he could read her at all. How much had she petted herself upstairs to place herself in such a state? Much to his shame, he had gone to bed and taken himself in hand, imagined her atop him, riding him, taking her pleasure.

He'd never come so fast and hard in his life.

"And if we're caught, are you accepting of the consequences of us dallying with each other? It would mean marriage, Victoria. It would mean your life of independence would be over."

She paced before him, debating his words for several moments before turning back to look at him. "I'm willing to take that risk. And I imagine marriage to you may not be so very boring if you allow me to do what I want."

He barked out a laugh, but all the while knowing he'd do whatever she wanted if it meant that he could have her as his.

"Where do you wish to start?" The words slipped from his mouth. He could not be about to do this. It was scandalous behavior.

She came over to him, pulling him from his chair. He stared down at her, amazed that by merely being beside her his blood quickened.

"Wherever you wish, so long as I find release."

Albert could not believe what she was saying. This could not be true. The one woman he longed for, wanted in his bed, to be his wife had not just asked him to make her climax.

He wished he knew exactly how to gain that ultimate end for her, but he did not. Nor could he ask his closest friend, her brother, how to manage it.

Damn it all to hell. He was literally living a nightmare caused by his own ineptitude.

"What are your thoughts on starting at the beginning? I fear if we do too much too soon, you may flee."

She shook her head, her chin rising defiantly. "I will never run away from something that I want."

Albert swallowed, thinking back to the books he'd read. Kissing was a good start, and they had already done that, and the act had been enjoyable. He would start there and move on from that position.

He brushed his lips against hers and she sighed into the embrace, soft and willing. Her tongue teased his lips, and he deepened the kiss, tangling his with hers, searing the feel of her into his mind forever. Her hands clutched at his lapels, no fear for what they were about to do, only passion.

They certainly came together with exquisite ease. How was he to rein in his desires when he wanted all of her? Marriage and a future. Hell, he'd welcome being caught if only it meant they would become man and wife.

All rational thought dissipated when he felt her hand atop his, pulling it from around her waist and placing it on her most private of places.

Albert stilled, breaking the kiss. "Victoria, this is too much. Too soon."

She shook her head. Her lips reddened and swollen from their kiss. "Touch me, Albert. Touch me here where I ache," she whispered.

It was all it took. Her plea and he was lost.

CHAPTER 16

*V*ictoria wasn't sure what had come over her, but what she did know was that she wanted Albert. She needed his touch, craved this sought-after release that the images teased them with. If she could find release by learning how to bring it onto herself, life would be so much sweeter.

It was scandalous of her. Her mother would never forgive her if she brought disgrace down upon all their heads, but she could not pull together the necessary caution to stop.

Albert's demanding kiss stole her wits. He was so very different to how she had always viewed him.

It was in one word... *Delicious.*

He kissed like a man starved. His little murmurings of pleasure, of need, spurred her to mimic him, kiss him back with all that he made her feel.

And it was quite a lot.

Her body was aflame. Her cunny was wet and weepy. She moved his hand from around her waist and placed it over her breast. The sensation made her knees tremble, and before she knew what was happening, Albert had scooped her up into his arms and sat on a nearby settee, placing her firmly across his legs.

Their tongues continued a dance of desire, seeking, teasing. His fingers ran along the top of her gown, teasing her flesh. Little goosebumps rose on her skin before he dipped one finger beneath her bodice.

She gasped, clutching at him as the pad of his finger grazed her nipple, taut and longing for touch. The sensation was wonderful and she wanted more of it.

The term greedy would suit her very well right now.

"That feels so wonderful." She pushed boldly into his hand like a cat after a pat.

"I ache to touch you." He kissed her cheek, jaw before moving down her neck, suckling at her earlobe. It tickled, and she giggled, undulating on his lap.

"More, Albert," she admitted, meeting his eyes quickly before he dipped his head to her neck, his lips sending a shiver of delight up her spine.

"I know that you do." He kissed his way across her bodice, his hands at her back, working the buttons on her dress. Within a moment or two, the gown gaped at the front, and Albert used the opportunity to push the bodice down, exposing her breasts.

Heat kissed her cheeks, even though she wanted him to see her. Wanted him to kiss where his finger had just teased. But she'd never been with a man that she had not been married to. As liberating and scary as that truth was, she did not stop him. Instead, she forced herself to relax and enjoy what was to come next.

Albert bent over one breast, his tongue flicking out to tease her pink, beaded nipple. Victoria clasped his face, holding him captive so he may never stop.

"Oh yes, Albert. More..."

His tongue flicked at her puckered nubbin before he

covered her with his mouth and suckled. The sensation spiked need between her legs, and she barely bit back a moan. She squirmed on his lap as his mouth lathed and teased her until she could stand it no longer.

"The other one, please," she implored him.

He pushed her down onto the settee, covering her. Albert took little time in pulling the gown down to her waist, exposing her fully.

"I have admired your breasts for some time. I could kiss them forever," he admitted.

Victoria enjoyed the admiration, reaching back and holding the settee armrest, flaunting herself to him with little embarrassment.

There was no time for awkwardness. Not anymore. Not when she knew he could make her feel alive. Something she had not felt for years.

"I am yours to do with as you please," she declared, her voice huskier than she'd ever heard it before.

Albert groaned, coming over her. Their lips met, held, and he took her mouth in a demanding, punishing kiss. Their tongues meshed, teeth mashed as the kiss turned wanton.

And then he was gone, his mouth over her second breast, his free hand teasing and kneading her other.

Victoria moaned, her body not itself. He teased her toward something that she'd never experienced before. It remained aloof, close, but not quite there.

"Melvin? Are you in there? I'm looking for Victoria, but I cannot find her. Have you seen her about the house?" The handle of the door rattled as Josh tried the latch several times. "Melvin? Did you hear me?"

They both stilled at the sound of her brother's voice. Albert moved first, wrenching off her and dragging her from the settee before she could fathom what was happening.

"Turn about. Your gown needs to be put to rights," he

whispered, physically turning her and pulling up her dress, his fingers working madly on the buttons of her gown.

"I won't be a moment," he yelled out to Josh. He turned her back around, cringing at the sight of her hair. Victoria reached up and realized several pins had fallen out.

"You need to hide." He looked about the room. Victoria did too but could see nowhere that she could remain hidden.

"In the window, there is a little ledge. Sit on that, and I'll cover you with the curtain."

She looked at the window. The ledge, if one could call it, was extremely narrow. "I do not think I will fit in there."

He ushered her over there, securing the last of her buttons as he did so. "You will." He pulled the curtain aside, helping her to sit on the seal, before he wrenched the curtain past her face, blocking her view from the room.

Victoria huffed out an annoyed breath, both because she was being hidden away but also because when she had entered this room, she had needed Albert. Now with her brother interrupting them, she was even more in need since they had not finished what they started.

She glanced down at her gown, correcting it more when she heard the lock of the door give way before it was opened.

Victoria recognized her brother's footsteps, holding her breath as he walked in and about the room, his steps coming too close to the window. She held her breath, expecting at any moment for the curtain to be wrenched aside, her brother's disappointed visage staring back at her.

"I do believe I saw Lady Victoria head out into the gardens after breakfast. Should we head outdoors and see if she is still taking the air or is on the terrace?"

For a man who prided himself on honesty, and there were no falsehoods when it came to Albert, he certainly knew how to fib very well. Had she not known the truth, even she would have believed such tales. Her brother did not reply straightaway but continued to walk about the room with a casualness that made her armpits damp. Did he suspect she was in the room? Is that why he had not left yet?

"The garden, you say?" Josh said, his footsteps determined once more, and headed toward the door. "Let us go and fetch her then. Mama wishes to leave soon for the picnic."

"Of course," Albert said, closing the door and leaving her alone.

Victoria bit her lip, having forgotten that they were to go for a carriage ride before lunch and picnic somewhere on Albert's estate afterward.

Retreating footsteps sounded down the hall, and Victoria took the opportunity to escape, leaving through the back of the house and using the servant's stairs to make her room, just as her mama came to fetch her.

"Ah, you're back from your walk. Very good, shall we go? I believe the carriage will be brought around soon."

Victoria picked up her bonnet and cardigan, forgoing the shawl, and followed her mama. She breathed a sigh of relief as they came downstairs, into the foyer just as her brother and Albert came in through the front door.

"Ah, there you are, sister. I have been looking for you."

"Not very well," her mama said, throwing her only son a warm smile. "She was in her room."

Her brother opened his mouth as if to say something but then thought better of it, holding out his arm to escort them to the carriage. "I must not have looked very well at all. Shall we?" he asked throwing Victoria a pointed stare.

Victoria dared not meet her brother's eye or look in the direction of Lord Melvin for fear of giving herself away.

She did, however, feel the heat of Albert's gaze burning down her spine as they made their way outside to the awaiting vehicle.

It seared her just as his touch had.

CHAPTER 17

They traveled a mile from the estate and stopped on the opposite side of the lake to Rosedale estate. Here they had a picturesque locality that ensured a better view of the Roman ruins that sat on the island on the lake.

Two footmen stood beside numerous blankets set out on the grass under the shade of an oak tree. The day was warm, with only the smallest bit of wind. As they made their way to the blankets, Victoria was thankful for the shade the old oak cloaked them in.

Albert and her brother talked incessantly about London, their estates, and improvements both of them wished to do over the coming months away from town. Not that Albert should have issues arranging repairs about his estate or on the tenant farms, for he rarely left Hampshire as it was. A gentleman was always accessible to his staff and farmers.

Victoria sat across from Albert, watching him, and knew that her mama watched her, but she no longer cared. The man intrigued her, and after his kissing and petting earlier today, she realized he quickened her blood like no other before him.

She turned her attention to the servant who opened the carriage door, helping her alight. They strolled to the blankets and sat, Victoria taking her time to set out her dress. Another odd thing for her to do. She'd never before wanted to impress any gentleman, but again, Lord Melvin made her preen.

It was utterly ridiculous since she had promised herself a future that included no husbands. No ties or children clinging about her skirts.

Paul had cured her of that absurdness, no matter how lovely Lord Melvin was turning out to be. Or how wicked his kisses.

She bit back a grin as Albert came and sat beside her, his warmth and presence making her stomach flutter. She cast him a look and found him watching her, his heated gaze warming her skin.

Her brother cleared his throat, passing her a glass of champagne before taking his seat with them all. The servants passed plates of food of cold meats and cheese, bread and tarts.

"There is a strawberry field just beyond, and also an olive grove that my mother planted during her first years of marriage. She had traveled to Italy as a child and enjoyed the little fruit. You're welcome to explore if you would like."

Her mother held out her hand to her brother. "Help me to stand, my dear. I should like to see the olive groves. I have heard of your mama speak of them at balls and parties and have long wanted to see what they were about."

Albert chuckled, the sound deep and gravelly. Had he always sounded so very handsome before? Could a voice be termed in such a way? After today, Victoria had to admit that it was possible.

"Would you care to join us?" Josh asked them.

Victoria shook her head, popping another lemon tart in

her mouth. "No, I would prefer to stay here in the shade. You go on. We will watch you from here."

Josh glanced at Albert, his eyes narrowing a little before turning and escorting their mama toward the olive trees. Was that a warning that passed between her brother and Albert? Maybe Josh had suspected her in the smoking room earlier today after all. She started when she felt Albert's hand cover hers, linking their fingers.

"I'm sorry that we did not get to finish what we started." His dark-blue eyes held hers, and she was powerless to look away. However was she to deny herself him when he was so very desirable? This was a complication in her life she had not planned on. Widow she wished to remain, but never a wife and she knew Albert would not abide having her as his mistress. "I long to be alone with you," he whispered.

Victoria took a calming breath. The memory of his hands, of what he had been doing to her before being interrupted, taunted her needy self. There was something serious misplaced within her. She could not turn into a wanton. Only lightskirts acted so, but here she was, a duke's daughter who could think of nothing but having Lord Melvin's clever mouth on her breasts, kissing and petting her aching flesh.

"Tonight, where should we meet?" She moved his hand to hide under her skirts, glancing behind her to see where the footmen were, happy to see they were over near the carriage taking their luncheon repast.

His eyes darkened, the muscle in his jaw clenched as she slipped his hand over her leg to her aching core, pushing him against her. Her dress hid most of what they were doing, but it could not hide her face, nor Albert's. Their ragged breathing, the need that shone in his eyes that she knew hers replicated.

He pushed against her, and she gasped, closing her eyes. Her body ached, thrummed, and she would do anything to be alone with him. Excited to see what else they would do when they were. She longed to be away from prying eyes so he could give her what she wanted.

"Oh," she gasped. He teased her in a circular motion. She longed to lie back upon the blankets, to open up to him, to let him have his way with her. So this was what she should have been doing with her hand in the bath…

How wonderfully wicked it would be when they could finish their interlude.

*A*lbert could not stop, nor could he tear his hand from her cunny. Damn it. He was surely going to hell touching a lady in this way—his friend's sister. The duke would call him out, and rightfully so should he catch them. They were walking a fine line of both scandal and desire. He watched Victoria with something akin to awe. She was so beautiful, so innocent, and utterly reckless. He'd always known she had a little rebellion in her blood, but this… Taking his hand and placing it against her sex floored him.

She utterly spellbound him, and he wanted her.

A virgin he may be, but after being around her, he was starting to think that having sex, taking pleasure from each other would not be so hard after all. It was more natural than unnatural, especially when it was with a woman one desired more than anyone else in the world.

The sound of the duke laughing in the olive grove pulled him to his senses, and he moved away, fisting his hands in his lap. Not only to keep them off her person but to stop anyone from noticing his erect cock straining against his breeches.

"Meet me in my smoking room tonight as you did today," was all he said as Victoria's mother, the duchess, and brother rejoined them.

Thankfully they did not move back toward the carriage

for some time, content to finish lunch and the two bottles of champagne his cook had chilled and packed for them. Victoria stood and, taking her mama's arm, strolled about the area, looking at the olive grove herself.

Josh studied the champagne in his hand, a quizzical frown on his brow. Albert schooled his features, hoping that he did not suspect that he was overstepping his bounds with his sister. Which he certainly was doing. And tonight, would even more so.

"How is your courting of Victoria progressing? It seems she likes your company better than most. Why, before I left London when Armstrong's courtship had just begun, she never showed much emotion with the chap." The duke lay down on the blanket, watching his sister and mother promenade. "With you she's all smiles and laughter. A shame that Armstrong was not able to keep his cock in his own breeches. What a gem he lost the day he overstepped his bounds."

To be a duke's daughter and be cast off for a maid, was not something that was done to someone so high on the peerage ladder. Victoria did not deserve such treatment. No one did.

"She sees me as a project, I believe, more than a possible husband. I will continue to try and dissuade her of that ideal in the coming weeks."

"So long as your persuasion is chaste, I wish you well with your endeavors. But I will not have you use her for your own misdeeds, Melvin. Victoria is my sister, and I will protect her at any cost to others."

Albert swallowed. Friend or not, the duke would not take kindly should he find out what they had done already during their "tutoring". It was anything but a game for him, but for Victoria, he was not as certain. To her, he believed she still saw him as a little fun, a gentleman to help her gain her wants and desires and nothing more.

Even knowing this, he wanted her to have feelings for him, both physical and emotional. She was such an independent, strong woman and would be a well-fought-after and victorious lady to catch should he secure her heart.

"My intentions are honorable, I promise, Your Grace," he said, meaning every word. As for Victoria's intentions being so, he was uncertain at this moment. But time would tell, and he would either end up with the woman he adored, or he would be sporting a very broken heart that he feared would never recover.

CHAPTER 18

*V*ictoria bathed and dressed for bed later that night, wishing her mama and brother goodnight before locking herself away in her room. She had taken a silly risk this afternoon on their picnic. When she thought about what she had done, she still could not believe she had taken Albert's hand and placed it on her person. And not just anywhere on her body, but between her legs.

She slumped down on the settee before the fire in her room, glaring at the flames licking the wood. It was all Lord Melvin's fault when she thought about it in truth. He had left her in a state of need, more than she had when she'd come to his silly smoking room the first time.

When she could not find this pinnacle by herself, well, she had little choice but to make him find it for her.

She pursed her lips, wondering if it were late enough and if her family would be asleep by now. Josh had departed for the local town to try out the tavern and had attempted to persuade Albert to join him. Thankfully the marquess had cried off, stating he needed to catch up on some paperwork, but wished her brother a good evening.

Victoria stood and crossed to the door, impatience nagging at her. She slipped a dressing gown on and slippers and cracked the door open just a bit. The hall was dark. No candle burned in any of the sconces or candelabras. Only a small, flickering light illuminated from under her brother's door. Victoria made her way through the house, memory guiding her this time before she came to the smoking room door. Checking once again that she was alone, she looked up and down the hall and could see no one. Stealing into the room, she closed the door quickly behind her and found nothing. Not even Albert.

She frowned.

Where was he? No fire burned in the grate, and the room was dark, save for a little moonlight that stole through the windows.

Victoria called out to Albert, or whispered more like, but there was no response.

Had he reneged on his own plan and decided not to come and meet her?

She huffed out a breath, tracing her steps back to her room, not seeing anyone on her way. Where had he disappeared to? Disappointment stabbed at her as she climbed into bed. Lord Melvin would want a very good reason for standing her up, but somehow she knew he would not. No doubt her brother had persuaded him to go to the tavern. The idea of him there, surrounded by women looking for a little fun with a lord, left her uneasy. She glared into the darkness of her room, listening out for their return, the sound of horses, anything so she could confront him over his movements.

What was she thinking! He was not her husband. He owed her nothing. Still, it took her several hours to fall to sleep.

. . .

*A*lbert was foxed. The tavern room, rank with smoke, sweat, and the foulness of stale beer rent the air, and still, it was not as terrible as he thought a night out at a tavern would be.

Several gentlemen estate owners joined him and the duke, drinking, some whoring the night away upstairs. For an hour or so, Albert had lost sight of Josh, but then he returned, his cravat less poised, along with his hair.

The duke slumped into the chair beside him, grinning from ear to ear. "Lovely company here. I'm surprised that you do not darken these doors more often."

More often? Albert had never before stepped foot into the premises. That he was missing his rendezvous with Victoria because her brother would not take no for an answer also did not help his mood.

Even so, the beer was refreshing, company amusing, and to sit and watch the play of people had been enjoyable. As a writer, picking up people's nuances and mannerisms was always helpful.

"Look here, that woman over there. She is watching you keenly," the duke said, sipping his beer and grinning.

Albert shook his head, having no interest in the lady. "If I am to win your sister's hand, you should know that she would not approve of me being here or if she heard of me bedding any of the ladies selling their wiles tonight. I thought you would've known better, Your Grace."

The duke chuckled, leaning back in his chair. "Oh, I know better, but when there is fun to be had, what of it? And you're not married yet. What would it hurt?"

Albert did not like this talk or the thought of touching another woman, not when he wanted Victoria above all else. "I am content to drink beer with you, my friend, but that is all. I will not be sewing my seed around here this evening."

The duke watched him a moment before clapping him on the back. "That is very good then, my friend. I'm glad you would remain true to your course, that being my sister. I like you even more now than I did before."

"You were testing me?" he asked him, not entirely sure he liked to be tested. The room spun, and he clasped the table to steady himself.

"I have been, but you passed. Now, shall we have another drink?" the duke asked, summoning more beer.

Albert tried to dissuade His Grace of the notion of more alcohol, but then again, it was a very good brew, so why not.

*V*ictoria woke to the sound of doors slamming open before shutting just as loudly. She went and checked out in the corridor, her eyes widening at the sight that beheld her.

Her brother was nowhere to be seen, but Lord Melvin was standing before her door, his eyes glassy and unfocused, his body reeking of beer and smoke.

"I missed you tonight," he said, louder than he ought.

She shushed him, pulling him into her room and closing and locking the door behind him. "Be quiet. You'll wake Mama."

He stumbled over to the bed, lying down with an *oomph*. Victoria wasn't sure what she should do. Should she ring for her maid? Or try to maneuver him back to his room without anyone seeing.

For all that she would like him to touch her, she still did not wish to be anyone's wife. No matter how much being Lord Melvin's wife was becoming more and more appealing every day. He was kind and sweet. How could anyone's heart remain immune to such a gentleman?

He stared at her through eyes that struggled to stay open. "I missed you this evening."

Victoria crossed her arms, staying a good distance from him. "Yes, I know. I found the smoking room empty when I went down there, and you nowhere to be found," she said sarcastically. "But I can see what you've been up to tonight. I hope you enjoyed yourself, my lord."

He groaned, fighting to sit up. When he'd finally managed it, he reached for her, but she darted out of his reach. "Do not be angry, Victoria. I wanted to stay home. Your brother would not take no for an answer."

All understandable, and Josh did tend to get his way when he wanted something. "Well, I'm sure the women at the tavern were much more skilled than I am. I do not blame you for going out. You are a man, after all, and they seldom do anything that warrants gentlemanly behavior. My late husband no exception. You appear no different."

He clapped his hand over his heart. "You wound me, my darling Victoria. I did not sleep with anyone. Hell," he mumbled, flopping back down on the bed. "I've never slept with anyone, and I'm not about to start with a whore plying her trade."

His words comforted her and made her like him even more. "You should leave my room before you are caught in here alone with me."

He slumped an arm over his eyes, groaning. "Oh yes, better not be caught with me. Or you may be made to marry me, and what a terrible disaster that would be." He sat up, leaning on his knees. "If I had you in my bed every evening, Lady Victoria, let me assure you, it would be anything but terrible."

A shiver stole down her spine at his words, intoxicating as they were. His gaze burned up and down her nightshift, and she covered her breasts, realizing she wasn't wearing a dressing gown.

"You need to go now, Albert," she whispered, with one last plea for him to do as she asked before it was too late.

CHAPTER 19

*A*lbert wasn't sure why he was in Victoria's room, but what he did know was that it was spinning at an alarming rate, and he ought to leave. He was foxed, stank, even he could smell his clothing, yet he could not bring forth the energy to get up and go as Victoria asked.

Instead, she kept speaking, and he kept answering in the most inappropriate ways. Alcohol was not made for appropriate conversation. It would seem.

She clasped his hand, pulling at him. He wrenched her close, and she tumbled over him. His cock twitched, the breath in his lungs seized. Hell, she was pretty, so damn sweet that she made his jaw ache.

He reached up, sliding her golden locks behind one ear, needing to see her face. "You're so beautiful, Victoria. Do you know how beautiful you are to me?"

She bit her lip, shaking her head. "You're drunk, Albert. Can you even see straight, my lord?"

"Do not call me my lord. I'm Albert to you. Always Albert." He leaned up, closing the small space between them, and kissed her. She met him halfway, their mouths fusing, taking from the other in a kiss that stole what little wits he had left. Which, in his current state, were not many.

She undulated on him, her legs slipping over his hips, and he reached down, grinding her against his aching cock. Her ass was tight and small and made him instantly hard. She gasped through the kiss, moaned his name.

And then she moved, rolling her hips over his cock, the buckskin breeches he wore. The thin lawn nightgown no barrier to their needs. He held her there, helping her tease them both.

His cock ached, strained against the buttons. He wanted to release himself, take her, take them both to heights yet to be explored, but he could not. Certainly not tonight. He was a drunken lout, in his cups in her room. He would not stoop so low as to take her here like this.

"Oh," she gasped against his lips. "Albert. This feels..."

He slid against her core, the heat between their bodies scalding. "It feels good," he breathed, fighting the urge to come.

"You're so hard, and ahhh, I ache for you. Tell me, is this what happens when one has pleasure without intercourse?"

"Yes," he breathed, rolling over to settle between her legs. "I promise I shall not take you, but I need to be closer."

She nodded, giving him leave, and he wrenched up her gown, exposing her mons to his view. She glistened from desire, the scent of need filling his nostrils. Like the image in the book, he wanted to lay his lips against her flesh, kiss her, flick her sweet nubbin with his tongue until she cried out his name.

She tried to push her gown down. Her cheeks kissed with a rosy hue. "Do not be embarrassed. You're beautiful to me. All of you."

Albert leaned down, kissing her deep and long until he felt her relax under him. He broke the kiss, kneeling between her legs, and ripped at the buttons on his breeches. His cock sprang free, thick and long, and her eyes widened.

But the brave, curious Victoria he adored reached out and slid her finger along his length. Albert swallowed a curse, wishing her finger was her hand, wrapped around him, pulling him toward release.

He closed his eyes, reveled in her touch. No, he wished it was her mouth, suckling him, taking him deep in her throat.

He groaned. "Allow me to bring you pleasure," he pleaded, unsure what he would do should she say no.

She lay back and let him do what he willed. "I trust you," she said, her eyes burning pools of need watching his every move.

Albert guided his cock against her heat. It felt so good, too good to be bad, scandalous like it was. He slid against her, teased her engorged nubbin until they were both breathing hard, Victoria's legs wrapped about his waist, her arms holding him close as he kissed her, teased her. He wanted her to come, to soar under his touch.

She moaned, gasping and pushing, stretching and undulating against him with increasing ferocity. The feel of her against him, wet and wanton, left his wits to spiral.

He was so close. Just a few more strokes, and he would shatter.

"Albert," she gasped, her eyes opening wide and wonder crossing her features as she climaxed. Her fingers slid over his back, her nails scoring his skin.

He groaned and joined her, spilling his seed over her mons and stomach. Terribly crass, but he could not care. They had found release, together, and there was nothing more marvelous.

They lay like that for a time. Both lost to the euphoria of what they had done before he rolled and slumped beside her. Without urging, she turned on her side, staring up at him.

"That was utterly unexpected. I had no idea that was possible. You may think me naive, but Paul never did anything of the sort in our bedchamber. When he bothered to be there that is."

Albert hated the bastard even more for his treatment of Victoria. He pulled her closer.

He had no idea it could be like that either. When he'd taken himself in hand, it had never felt as good as it did just before with Victoria. Already, the thought of her made his cock twitch, and he wanted her again.

He smiled, meeting her wondrous gaze. "It has never felt like that for me before either. You had better take care, my lady, or I shall become addicted to you, and there will be no getting away from me then."

She chuckled, stretching out across the bed. "It is you, Lord Melvin, who ought to be careful, or I'll make you my mister."

He barked out a laugh, and yet at her words, a little hope expired within him. How could she share her body so intimately and still only see him without any emotional connection? He certainly wanted more from whatever it was that they were doing—tutoring him in how to be a good husband. He did not want to be a good husband to anyone unless that anyone was Victoria.

"It is you who ought to be careful, or you'll be made my wife." A little crow of satisfaction shouted in his mind when she paused at his words. He would not look upon tonight as a misguided, utterly reprehensible action that he'd done, but a step to making her see they fit like kid leather gloves. She may not see just yet, but she would. He would win his Victoria still, and tonight had been the first official stepping stone along that path.

. . .

*T*he following morning Victoria sat at the breakfast table and fought not to think about what the marquess, who sat at the head of the table eating bacon, eggs, his steaming-hot black coffee to the side, had done to her.

What they had done together last night in her room.

Her stomach knotted at the memory of her release. It had been different to her times with Paul. The intensity had been higher with Albert, even thinking about it now made her squirm. Her body had broken free at that moment. She had become a woman free of restraint, of wifely duties. She was simply a woman who had found pleasure with a man, and it was Lord Melvin who had driven her there.

She stirred her tea, wondering how they could go forward after such an event, how she would steer her instruction of him toward finding a wife and not toward finding a vacant room in the house and making him make love to her.

"Darling, I think your tea is stirred," her mama said, pulling her from her thoughts. She dropped the spoon, and it clattered on the small dish the cup sat on.

Heat crept up her neck, and she looked to where Albert sat and maddeningly found him behind his paper, ignoring the commotion she had made.

"Apologies," she said, her brother watching her intently. Victoria picked up her tea and sipped it, a congenial smile pinned on her lips. "What are we doing today, Mama? Should we travel into the village and cast our eyes over the shops?"

"That sounds like a lovely idea, my dear. I shall have our carriage brought around after breakfast."

"May I join you?" Albert asked, folding his paper and laying it on the table. "I feel as though I have not been out of the house in an age."

117

"Really?" Victoria queried sweetly. "I thought you and my brother were out only last evening?"

Her mama cast a curious glance at Josh before turning her attention to Lord Melvin. "Did my son take you out last evening, Lord Melvin? I hope he was not too much of a bad influence on you," she teased.

Josh sputtered, affronted. "I would never be a bad influence on my oldest friend. We had a beer at the local tavern, and it was an enjoyable night all around."

"It was indeed," Albert said, his gaze catching hers quickly.

Need, hot and senseless, thrummed through her, and she wished they were alone. Victoria swallowed, schooling her features. "We shall be looking for a modiste, my lord. Are you sure that is what you would like to escort us to?"

Albert's lips twitched. "I shall accompany you if only to escort you as I should since you are my guests. I will, however, leave the modiste up to you to visit alone."

"I wonder if they have any gowns fit for the country dance, Mama. I do not wish to look too high in the instep."

Her mother raised her brow. "Really, Victoria, your gowns are lovely and new. While we shall look, I do not think you need a new wardrobe."

Victoria stared out the window in the breakfast room. She had not been looking for a new wardrobe, just a gown that was less opulent than the ones she owned. She would stand out against the townsfolk and local gentry, and as much as she adored her family, sometimes blending in helped a little. Made one's night much more pleasant, and she wanted to be approachable for Lord Melvin's potential brides. If they were scared of speaking to her, she would not be able to vet them for the position of his wife.

CHAPTER 20

*A*lbert greeted some of the townsfolk who wished him good morning as he strolled before the modiste's window waiting for Victoria and the duchess.

The groom held the horses while the driver sat atop the box, waiting patiently for them all. He wasn't so patient. He needed to speak to Victoria and be alone with her if he could manage such a thing before expiring. He did little these days but think of her, and tonight he would have to make an effort to ride out to his hunting box and get some words down on his next manuscript. The muse was well alive within his mind, Victoria giving him plenty of ideas and plot fodder to write onto the page. It would also help keep his hands off her person, which he was wont to do at any opportunity that arose.

He started back up the pebbled path before the shops and inwardly groaned when he spotted Miss Nancy Eberhardt, only daughter and heiress to a local gentleman and whose mother had passed during her birth. The young woman was pretty and sweet-natured, all the elements a gentleman would want in a wife, but unfortunately for Nancy, he had never had eyes for her.

The only woman he'd ever taken note of was currently looking at gloves near the window of the modistes.

Miss Eberhardt spied him and smiled warmly. He bowed when she came to stand before him, her broad smile and bright eyes putting him on guard. Her maid, a sickly little creature, stood back, demure and quiet as always.

"Lord Melvin, how wonderful to see you about. I was only telling Papa the other day that the townsfolk do not see you enough. What brings you here today? You look as if you're loitering about if I'm honest." She chuckled.

He smiled, gesturing to the store. "I'm merely escorting my guests to the modiste."

Miss Eberhardt's face lost a little of its brightness at his words. "Oh, you have guests? Do I know them?"

Albert had little idea if she knew Victoria or was associated with the Duke of Penworth's seat. "My good friend, The Duke of Penworth is staying, along with his sister and mama."

"Lady Victoria is here?" She smiled, looking toward the shop windows. Albert did the same and could not see Victoria anymore.

"She is, yes."

Miss Eberhardt clapped her gloved hands, her smile back on her pretty visage. "I shall love to see her again. As you know, Papa fell ill during the last few weeks of the Season, and we had to return home early. I was unable to meet with her before we left."

"I did not know that. I hope Mr. Eberhardt is doing better now?" he queried, liking the older gentleman, his straight talk and no use for nonsense, similar to himself in that regard.

"He is doing much better, thank you."

Just then, the door to the modiste opened, and Victoria stepped outside. Her attention slipped from him to Miss Eberhardt. "Nancy?" she queried. "I did not know you lived in Camberley. How did I not know that?" Victoria said, pulling Miss Eberhardt into a quick embrace.

Albert watched with interest, not knowing the two ladies were acquainted and looked to be close friends.

"We're situated but a mile from here and from Lord Melvin's estate. I did not know you were staying close by, or I would have called on you." Miss Eberhardt clasped Victoria's hand, squeezing it. "How are you? I feel we have so much to catch up on."

Victoria chuckled, her eyes bright with pleasure. "I am very well and all the more pleased at having seen you again."

"I see you are visiting our local modiste," Miss Eberhardt stated. "Were you able to purchase anything in the store to your liking?"

"A dress for the country dance. Are you attending?"

Miss Eberhardt's eyes brightened, and she all but bounced where she stood. "I am, yes. How wonderful that you'll be there. We shall catch up properly."

"You're more than welcome to visit me at Rosedale. I should like some female company other than Mama." Albert smiled at her teasing. How he admired her. She was so friendly and warm, so different to other ladies of his acquaintance of lesser rank when speaking to others. And Miss Eberhardt, no matter how wealthy, had no peerage in her family, no titles or elevating connections, and yet still, Victoria treated her like an equal. A friend.

He marveled at her. Admiring her all the more for her warmth and good heart.

"If you're in agreement with that, my lord?" she asked him.

Albert smiled at them both, knowing that he would do

TAMARA GILL

anything if it meant that it made Victoria happy. "Of course, you're welcome to visit."

"Thank you, my lord," Miss Eberhardt watched him for longer than he would term appropriate before she turned her attention back to Victoria.

He hoped she did not have romantic designs on him. As much as he liked the young woman, she had never stirred his blood. He had always seen her as a affable acquaintance, but not for him.

"We shall be home the day after tomorrow if you would like to luncheon with us," he offered.

"I would love that very much." Miss Eberhardt's attention shifted past him, and he turned to see her father waiting in a carriage. Albert gave a cursory wave to the gentleman.

"I must be off, but I shall be at Rosedale the day after tomorrow."

"It was lovely seeing you again, Nancy," Victoria said, sincerity echoing in her words.

"And I you. Both of you," Miss Eberhardt said, casting one last smile at Albert before she was off.

He ignored Victoria's stare, and the knowing grin on her lips that he could discern from the corner of his eye. He opened the carriage door, helping her up. He followed her, seating himself beside her.

"You look very beautiful today. I have missed you," he said, reaching for her hand.

Her fingers entwined with his, her eyes darkening with a need that he too felt. Would it always be this madness, this undeniable want that sizzled between them? If they were alone, her mother not mere feet away from them in the store, he would be tempted to wrench her into his arms and kiss her soundly.

"I did not think you would remember last evening. You were hardly in the state to have such a sound memory."

"I may have been foxed." He picked up her hand and kissed her gloved fingers. "But I remember everything of what we did."

"Really?" she teased, pursing her lips. "What did we do. Remind me?"

He pushed down on the need that ran wild and hot through his blood at her words. Memories of her crying out as he made her come, as his cock slid against her cunny left him hard and aching.

He leaned toward her, his lips but a breath from her ear. "I made you come. I want to make you scream my name, maybe even one day in a carriage." He felt her shiver, the small gasp of shock at his words.

The door to the shop tinkled its little bell, notifying them the duchess had left. Albert sat back just as the groom opened the door for the duchess. He offered his hand to Her Grace. "Let me help you," he suggested.

The duchess took his hand and settled herself across from them, two small packages placed beside her by the groom.

"Your gown will be delivered tomorrow, not that I think you needed another, but now that I've seen what they had, the best for a country dance such as the one we will attend, I understand your plight."

"Thank you, Mama," Victoria said.

Victoria's reply revealed not an ounce of her being affected by his words, his touch of just before. How was it that she could remain so calm and unaffected?

He could not be further from such a stance.

"I am looking forward to the dance. It has been many years, not since before my coming out, that I have attended such an event." The duchess's words were warm at the memory.

"I saw Miss Eberhardt, Mama. She lives close by and will be attending the dance and calling on us the day after tomorrow." Victoria considered Albert a moment, and he fought not to fidget under her gaze. "She's a lovely woman of means and will do well as a wife. Although, since her papa is a widower, I think she would be happily settled if she were close by to her home."

Albert inwardly groaned, already foreshadowing where Victoria's thoughts were taking her and who she thought quite perfect for his future bride.

He did not comment on her words, not wanting to be rude, but Miss Eberhardt, no matter how aggregable, was not for him.

"Do you not concur, Lord Melvin?" Victoria asked him, her innocent smile hiding a devious matchmaking mind he did not particularly like.

"Miss Eberhardt is a kind, considerate woman. I wish her well with whomever she marries. I'm sure she will make him very happy." But it would not be him.

Victoria's eyes narrowed, and he ignored her ire, deciding this conversation was over, and the view outside the carriage window was much more to his liking.

CHAPTER 21

"hat is wrong with Nancy, Albert? She is quite perfect for you. She is from Hampshire, her father lives close by, and she's an heiress. If one dare says it, I would suggest she is the answer to your prayers. You ought to court her at the forthcoming country dance, see if you have anything in common other than your wealth and similar upbringing. You may be pleasantly surprised and find you like her very much."

After finding him ensconced here after they had returned from the village, Victoria slumped down on the settee in Albert's library. He had been oddly quiet on the way back to Rosedale in the carriage, and even though she and her mama had kept the conversation going, she could not help but wonder if he was put out with her in some way.

He did not look up from where he sat at the desk, looking over a pile of letters and estate account books. She may be interrupting him, but she could not leave him now. Not when they were so close to finding him the perfect woman to fill the position of a wife in this beautiful house. He would be a fool indeed to let such a wonderful opportunity such as Nancy slip through his fingers.

Victoria did not know a nicer or sweeter-natured woman in London. Other than her sisters, of course.

He sighed, throwing the quill onto the ledger open before him with more force than necessary, spilling a little of the ink. "I have already stated I am not interested in Miss Eberhardt in a romantic sense. Had I been, with us living in such close proximity, I would have already courted her to see if she returned my affections, Victoria. Please know that I shall not be pursuing her."

Victoria came over to the desk, leaning against it. She narrowed her eyes on him, not understanding why he was such a pain about it all. "You wanted my help in finding you a wife. Of teaching you how to go about courting a lady and being less awkward and shy around them. You did very well this morning with Miss Eberhardt. You are improving daily. I do not understand what we're doing if you're not going to take my advice when a suitable lady steps before you."

He leaned back in his chair, running a hand through his hair. She ignored the flutter the action made in her stomach or how ruggedly, flusteredly handsome he looked right at this moment. How could anyone not want to marry him?

Albert was a hidden gem among all the rough stones in society for all his nervousness around women.

Then why do you not have him for yourself?

Victoria thrust the thought aside. Her future was secure, set, and she had already started planning her first trip abroad. That travel did not include a husband and a gaggle of babies holding her back. Marriage was a mistake she would never make again.

"I do need your help in helping me navigate courtship with a woman. I did well today because I have known Miss Eberhardt for many years, and while I do not like her romantically, she is a friend. That is the only reason why I did so well. Place me in London, and you will see how awkward I still am."

Victoria wiggled to sit up on his desk, scrunching up some of the papers beneath her skirts. "Is there no one that you already know who you think will suit? You must be open to meeting new people, making connections for this to work."

"I am open to the possibility, but Miss Eberhardt is not one of them. I'm sorry to disappoint her if she harbors feelings for me. Mine are what they are, Victoria. You would not like to be forced toward a gentleman you only saw as your friend, would you not?"

"Well, no," she admitted.

"If I," he said, standing and coming to stand before her, "followed you about at every ball, forced my affections on you when you did not return them, you would dislike it very much. It is no different."

She supposed he had a point, but still, a small niggling worry kept poking at her mind that Albert viewed her as his future wife, the woman he wanted and he should not. Her heart was no longer capable of such trust, not with Albert or anyone. She thought she had known her late husband. She hadn't known him at all. Albert wanted children, a wife content to live in the country. She was none of those things. The world had opened up to her as a widow. She could not run back down the aisle to repeat a mistake that had humiliated her more than even her family knew.

"Very well, I shall try and help you dissuade Miss Eberhardt in thinking there is a future between you, but you must promise me that you will try with someone."

His lip twitched into a devilishly handsome grin. Victoria found herself reaching for the lapels of his jacket, pulling him close. Realizing her mistake, she dropped her hands, mentally chastising herself for giving him ideas of them.

"Thank you," he said before striding for the door and leaving her sitting on his desk to watch him go. She frowned after him, unsure if she was put out or relieved by his departure.

Stupid fool that she was, she did not know which one it was.

*L*ater that evening, when everyone was abed, Albert stole out to the stables, saddled his gelding, and rode out to his hunting lodge. He was behind on his words and needed to get down several pages before he fell behind on his deadline.

The lodge was quiet and dark, and he took a few moments starting the fire and lighting almost all the candles he had there, needing light above all else. He would normally travel down here through the day and leave before nightfall or just after, but due to his guests, his routine was all at odds.

He sat down at his desk, the words flowing from his fingers for several hours, his mind transported to the dark, dank streets of London, the story taking a menacing turn where the heroine was in search of the hero after footpads had kidnaped him.

The sound of birds chirping pulled him from his pages, and he looked up to see the kiss of dawn on the landscape outside. He leaned back in his chair, stretching and yawning, wondering how he would get through the day playing host while needing to sleep.

"Albert? Are you out here?"

He swore at the sound of Victoria's voice, throwing the manuscript pages into a leather folder and locking it away in the bookshelf behind him.

He went over to the decanter of whiskey, drinking from the bottle to freshen his mouth just as the door opened. Victoria poked her head around the wood, a warm smile forming on her lips.

"Ah, so this is where you were hiding all night. I did try to find you to partake in more lessons but could not locate you. A servant told me you had ridden out to the hunting lodge."

What was he to tell her? That he wrote the very books she loved to read out here? That he was her favorite author? Albert chose neither.

"I needed to check on the lodge. There have been reports of poachers and thieves in the area," he lied, having never cared if people walked his grounds and took wildlife from him to feed their families.

She closed the door behind her, walking about the lodge and taking in the thick Aubusson rugs under her leather boots. She was wearing trews again and her tight riding jacket that accentuated her figure. The kiss they shared the last time she was attired so rose up in his mind and he took a calming breath, cooling his desire.

He followed her progress with something akin to a man starved of sustenance. He was starting to think he was a little obsessed with winning her love.

She flopped down onto a settee, kicking off her boots and undoing the buttons on her riding jacket, throwing it aside. She wore a white linen shirt beneath, hemmed prettily with lace. "This is as good a place as any for more lessons." She reached into a bag that he had not seen over her shoulder, pulling out the book of sketches of sexual positions.

She opened it to the last page they had looked upon. "I thought we should start here, Albert. Discuss what I liked about what you did to me the other evening, and how perhaps what you can have with your wife when the time comes."

He inwardly groaned but joined her, sitting close by, reveling in the fresh scent of her. Had she bathed already so early this morning? He wanted to kiss her, kiss her skin and see for himself if she tasted as sweet as she smelled.

"Very well," he agreed. Feeling bold, he pointed to the sexual act of the man kissing the woman between her legs. "I should like to know if my wife would enjoy such touch. Would you be brave enough to let me practice on you, Victoria?"

He held his breath, knowing it was wrong what he was asking her. He ought to be horsewhipped. Her brother ought to put a bullet through his skull, and still, he did not back down. Merely waited for her to reply.

Her chin rose defiantly, and he knew her answer before she uttered it. Of all her siblings, Victoria was never the one to back down from a challenge, certainly if it were asked as such.

"Of course. I said I would help you, and I will. Shall we start now?"

Liquid-hot desire rushed through his veins, and he stood, pulling her to stand. "Let me help you with these," he stated, untying the buttons on her breeches. Dear God, she was magnificent, and the idea of what they were about to do was beyond his dreams. He just hoped he performed it as well as she hoped. He would hate to disappoint his future bride.

CHAPTER 22

*W*hat on earth was she doing? She should not be allowing such intimate acts with a gentleman she had no intention of marrying. But the dark, hungry gaze of Albert's pushed away her nervousness and allowed a boldness she never thought she would possess to take charge.

Even if she were known in her family as bold and outspoken, she was not a woman of loose morals. Not until Albert Kester came into her world. Being a widow had made her lose her sense of morals.

With a care that left her trembling, he flicked open the last of the buttons on her breeches and slid them down her legs. Victoria watched as he took a calming breath, a muscle working at his temple with each beat of his heart.

Her own pumped fiercely as she let him start with the ties at the neck of her shirt. There were only three before he lifted it from her body, and she was left with nothing but a corset and shift beneath.

"You may sit back down," he suggested, his voice deep and raspy as if the words were hard to speak.

She did as he asked, gasping when he kneeled between

her legs, pushing them open with a determination she did not expect from him. Victoria bit her lip, wondering what this was going to be like. How on earth was she allowing such liberties with her body? Albert had muddled her mind in more ways than she first thought.

His large hands and strong fingers slid up her legs, massaging her muscles as he glided ever closer to her sex. Her body ached, her senses alive and needy.

She realized with no small amount of shock that she wanted to see his mouth on her, watch him make her reach pleasure as they had the other night.

His hands grasped the backs of her knees, and he pulled her toward the edge of the settee. His heavy-lidded eyes fixed on her core, and he licked his lips. Victoria let out a huff of breath, having not expected to like his reaction to her so much.

"You're so beautiful, Victoria. I ache to taste you."

Her eyes spied the book, open on the page of the sexual act they were about to perform, and she shivered.

He kissed her leg with slow, torturous strokes, and Victoria moaned with need. She was so open to him, a shiver of vulnerability stole through her, hoping that he approved of what he saw, would not shy away from her after they did what they were about to do.

Although she did not want to marry, she did enjoy Albert's company, liked him very much. She wanted to help him, but something told her that nothing would ever be the same again after they did what they were to do.

Would she be able to walk away from him, stand by and watch him marry another? Know that he would make love to another lady night after night, and that lady would not be her?

He kissed along her leg, his warm breath marking her skin. His fingers flexed on her thighs, pushing her wider. He marveled at her a moment before dipping his head. She gasped, biting her lip as his lips touched her, and then his tongue flicked out, caressing her most private flesh.

Victoria leaned back, closing her eyes, reveling in his touch. He kissed her, flicked her aching, throbbing nubbin with his tongue before suckling and sending her wits to flee. His mouth devoured her, taking his fill. His muffled moans of enjoyment met her ears, and he kissed her cunny with abandon.

It was too much. Too wonderful. How had she never known with her husband that such acts were possible. For all of Paul's rakish wiles, he knew very little at all. Or did not want to do these things with her.

She pushed the unhelpful, hurtful thoughts aside, lifting herself toward his mouth. Ignoring the wantonness of her action. He scooped her legs over his shoulders, taking her with a need that surpassed any she'd ever known.

Victoria reached down and ran her fingers into his hair, holding him to her, grinding herself on his face like a woman out of her mind. And perhaps she was a little out of her mind with need.

Pleasure teased her senses. She was hot, clammy, and wanted to shatter to a million pieces. Albert flicked his tongue across a sensitive place, and finally, she tumbled over the edge. Stars burst behind her eyes, and she undulated against him, not caring how she looked, how much she moaned, his name a chant of pleasure.

He kept her against him as the last tremors of her release echoed through her body before ending how he began, kissing along her legs, watching her through heavy-lidded eyes that burned with his own need.

Victoria could not move. Every muscle felt lax and as heavy as a case of gold. Albert reached over, taking a rug from the settee, and laid it over her legs as he came to sit beside her, picking up the book that lay on the floor.

"What did you think, Victoria? Should I not disappoint my future wife?"

Victoria shook herself free of the muddling pleasure that cloaked her to what Albert was saying. Disappoint his wife? The idea made ice run through her veins. She sat up, taking the book and flipping the pages, anything but to dissect why it was his words upset her so much.

"I think your wife will be most pleased, and today, when we return to the house, we shall sit down and play cards, learn how to interact together in that setting. It is not only in the art of lovemaking that you require tutelage. You also need to feel confident and sure when hosting and courting during the season. We cannot lose ourselves in this way when there is still so much to learn."

"Instead of cards, what do you think if we partook in an archery contest? Or lawn games. There is a chance next season that I will host a house party here at Rosedale, and I know ladies like to take part in that pastime."

"We can do that too. We have a few days to fill before the country dance, but tonight I think cards would be best."

"Whatever you think," he said.

Victoria shuffled out of the chair and dressed quickly. She could not look at him, achingly aware that he watched her every movement. Just as she, too, was aware of him and his presence. The memory of her climax an occasion she doubted she'd ever forget.

Albert was taking up too much time in her mind, but she could not help herself. Whenever she saw him, she wanted to be near him, even if only to converse and spend time. If that conversation and time led to pleasurable interludes, then all the better.

It was out of character and unhelpful to her plans.

She wrenched on her boots, tying them quickly before looking about for her riding jacket. She stilled, swallowing the need that coursed through her blood when she spotted Albert holding it aloft with one finger, a small smile playing about his lips.

He was a devil, and he knew it. He was also becoming quite the rogue. Well, what she assumed a rogue was like. Men of that ilk seduced ladies in hunting lodges during daylight hours.

Which reminded her, if she did not return to the house soon, she would be missed at breakfast, and her mama would be concerned or suspicious.

Victoria stepped over to him, taking the jacket, and slipped it on. "Thank you. I shall see you back at Rosedale."

"Is that all?" he queried, his brows raised.

Nerves fluttered in her stomach. "What else do you want?"

He growled, wrenching her close. He took her lips, and all thoughts of getting out of there, away from him, vanished. Victoria kissed him back, tasting the tart taste of herself on his lips. It was not displeasing. If anything, it made her long for more of what they had started with each other.

He broke the kiss, his eyes dark and stormy with need. "I want everything, Victoria."

Victoria chuckled, but her insides seized with panic. What did everything mean? Did he want a future, to marry her, for her to have his children, and a life together? She wanted none of those things, not after her disastrous first marriage. The idea of being anyone's property, to be treated with no respect revolted her sensibilities. She shook her head, an impossibility she could never do again.

But a life with Albert would be different. You are different around him.

Victoria stepped out of his hold, striding to the door, and

the freedom the outdoors beckoned. "I want lots of things too, but I do not always gain them. I shall see you back at the house," she called over her shoulder, shutting the door on his handsome, if not disappointed, face.

Their little tutoring game was getting out of hand. Emotions were becoming involved and awful and alarming as it was, Victoria was not sure that it was all Lord Melvin who was feeling them.

CHAPTER 23

*A*lbert strode back into the foyer of Rosedale and directly into the path of the Duke of Penworth. Penworth greeted him warmly before they started for the parlor upstairs.

"I saw Victoria earlier at breakfast," His Grace stated. "She mentioned you were hosting a card night this evening. Would you mind if I invited some local friends, gentry that I know in this area, and you too, I should imagine?"

Albert rang the bell for tea as they entered the room, warming himself before the fire since the day had turned cooler than expected. "You may invite whomever pleases you. Anyone in particular?"

"Lord and Lady Hammilyn are at home and are close enough to attend. They will, of course, wish to bring their daughter. I hope that it suitable."

"I give you leave to use my desk to write to them. Have a groom ride over and deliver it. I should think they will attend."

Penworth sat on a nearby chair, crossing his legs as a

footman came in with tea and biscuits. "I will pour, thank you," Albert said to the servant, dismissing him.

He poured Penworth a cup before doing the same for himself before settling down on the chair opposite his friend. "I cannot help but wonder if your interest in Lord Hammilyn has anything to do with his daughter, which from what I hear is a beauty and one that many a young buck are looking forward to seeing next season in town."

Penworth shrugged, sipping his beverage. "I have never laid eyes on the chit, and I would never marry a woman so young."

"Ah, but remember, Lady Sophie is not so young. She spent several years abroad with her brother, who lives in Spain with his wife. They will return, of course, when he inherits, but until then, I believe they live in Cadiz."

Penworth frowned at this information, clearly confused. "How old is she?" he asked, unable to mask the curiosity in his words.

"I believe she is two and twenty."

"A perfect age for you, Lord Melvin. Maybe you will go into a contest with my brother and court Lady Sophie yourself."

Albert coughed, choking on his tea, having not known Victoria was listening to their conversation. She waltzed into the room. The scent of lavender soap and her usual perfume of jasmine wafted through the air. Albert fought not to take a noticeable breath, the memory of what they had done only hours before clear in his mind.

Penworth grinned but did not comment as his sister sat. "What else are you two gentlemen discussing other than the ladies you're going to court?"

"Nothing of interest, merely the card games to be played this evening. I thought to invite Lord and Lady Hammilyn and their daughter, who Melvin tells me is back from abroad. Do you know Lady Sophie, Victoria?" her brother asked.

She shook her head, leaning back on the settee, clasping a nearby pillow, and holding it on her lap. The scene was reminiscent of a domesticated family enjoying the morning together. Albert could imagine such a vision of Victoria joining him for tea, discussing future events at Rosedale with visitors such as her brother. He watched her, sipping his drink and wishing he could convince her that to be married to him would not be a chore. That he would do everything in his power to make her happy and content, even if that meant they traveled for years before starting a family. Convince her that he would never break her heart.

"I do not know her at all. Although I do believe Elizabeth may have met her some years ago."

Josh finished his tea, placing the cup on the table before them. "I shall write to them and hope that they will attend. You would like Lord Hammilyn, Victoria. He has wolfhounds like you."

She grinned at her brother, her eyes lighting up at the mention of her favorite breed of dog. "Oh, well, I shall like him very much, and I will always have a conversation subject to swing to should the worse happen, and I find dreaded silence has ensued between us."

"Just right," Penworth said, standing. "I shall be back soon. But I want to get that missive off before it grows too late."

Albert listened as the duke made his way down the hall, heading to the library downstairs.

"Is something the matter?" he asked her at her silence, hoping he had not pushed her too far out at the hunting lodge. When she had turned up at his door there, he had not expected they would progress to such acts, but now that they had, he would never regret their actions.

He wanted her as his wife. He would seduce his wife with actions similar to what he had performed on her. There was no shame in that. Not unless she refused him when he gained enough confidence to breach the taboo subject that she seemed to detest.

She shook her head, but worry clouded her emerald eyes. "Not particularly, but I do think you ought to consider Lady Sophie for your wife. Tonight if she attends, you must try to use the tools that I have given you to see if there is a connection there."

"And if your brother is interested in the lady?"

"Then you shall both try, and we shall all see who the victor is. But you do not have to marry her this evening, merely see if she is pleasant and suitable to your character. Suppose you can converse with her without getting tongue-tied and anxious all the better. I shall be there with you too. I shall not let you fail."

A cold, hard stone lodged where his heart beat. "You are determined as ever to have me married before the end of the next Season. Not every female that I meet is someone whom I want to shag for the rest of my life."

Her cheeks heated, and he was glad of it. He frowned, starting to dislike being pushed toward women he had no interest in whatsoever. He knew whom he suited, whom he adored and wanted by his side for the rest of his life, and it was the very woman telling him to marry another.

"I know that. I'm merely trying to help. You did agree to my aid."

"Of course," he acknowledged. "But can I not tell you should I find a woman who sparks my interest and then move forward with a plan? This throwing women at my head at any available turn is starting to grow weary."

"But we have only just started, and we're only using these

women as practice. Do not be so prickly, Lord Melvin. I am only trying to assist you."

"And I suppose you are still determined to die old and alone, never marrying due to being broken hearted by an ass."

She gasped, and he regretted his hard words immediately. "Victoria, I—"

"Right, the letter is off to Lord Hammilyn. I should think they will attend. When I ran into him yesterday in the village, he was doing nothing but rusticating at home."

"Sounds delightful," Albert mumbled, watching Victoria, who sat glaring at him. "I shall have cook do a light supper this evening instead of a meal."

"That sounds just the thing," Penworth said, sitting back down on the chair he vacated only minutes before with not a clue his sister and friend were at odds.

"Cheer up, Victoria. Lady Sophie will be good company for you. Keep you occupied since I know you tend to grow bored."

"I'm not bored," she said defensively, throwing a quick look in Alberts's direction.

He poured himself another tea, wishing it were something stronger like whiskey or brandy. He could use a little fortification right about now. Should Victoria grew bored did not bode well for his plans and hopes. Would she find life here at Rosedale beyond her endurance? Would she never settle or always wish for adventure?

He would love to travel if he found the right woman to go with, but he could not be away constantly. His estate, his writing required him to be in England several times a year. The idea of them, of being her husband, grew ever smaller in his mind's eyes, edged a little further out of reach.

"You could have fooled me," Josh teased, grinning. "Maybe

while you're trying to fix up Melvin or myself with Lady Sophie, you could think about your own future. Of who else in London would suit you now that you're available once again."

"No one will suit me." She shot out of her chair, striding for the door, her gown swishing about her legs as her forceful steps carried her away. "I'm going to die old and alone without family. That is what I'm going to do. To hell with men and their needs for a family and bed partner. I'd rather love myself, trust in only myself before anyone else."

"Victoria, that is uncalled for," Josh said, standing, scowling at his sister, who stormed down the hall before a door slammed somewhere in the depths of the house. Her bedroom door Albert supposed.

"I do apologize, Melvin. I say I was only teasing her. I do not know what could be upsetting her so."

Albert knew what had sparked such a temper, but he could not be sorry for it. The truth sometimes hurt, and that she continuously told him no, that she did not want him for herself, no matter how much pleasure they may give each other. How well they got along. At some point, he would have to accept that truth and move forward.

"Do not concern yourself. I'm sure she will be back to rights this evening. We're all entitled to a moment or two of temper."

"I suppose," Penworth said, frowning at the door his sister had left through. "But I am interested in seeing what this rumored beauty Lady Sophie looks like. Let us hope she has a pleasant disposition as her face is said to be."

Albert smiled, but inside, his gut churned, hating the fact Victoria was angry and upset. That was not supposed to happen. He never wished for her to be so. "I think you shall be pleased, Penworth. Maybe it is not I who will marry first after all my schooling, but you."

Penworth chuckled, shaking his head. "She would have to be a rare gem to tempt me, but we shall see."

"That we shall," Albert agreed. "Tonight."

CHAPTER 24

*A*lbert made sure to pay attention to their guests, especially Lady Sophie, whose beauty had caught him unawares. She had grown in height and beauty since he'd seen her last. Granted, she had been quite a distance from him when he had spied her.

Even so, Penworth continued to remain amusingly tongue-tied when around the woman. Which, if anything, made being near her entertaining. Not that he wanted the chit for himself. He was only talking to her more than he would normally because Victoria had asked him to.

Victoria stood beside her mother, watching his every word. He studied Victoria a moment, unable to make out if her visage was one of curiosity or displeasure.

He hoped it was the latter. That him talking to Lady Sophie, who next year would certainly be a success in London, vexed her. More the truth of the matter was that she found fault in his conversation and was working out how to correct him when they were alone.

"Are you looking forward to next season, Lady Sophie? I

understand you're making your debut," Albert said, surprised by his confident tone. Mayhap Victoria's lessons were working in his favor.

"Not particularly. If you were in my shoes, Lord Melvin, would you care to be auctioned off to the highest bidder? I think not."

He bit his tongue, fighting to keep the laugh that wanted to bubble up and out of him.

Penworth wasn't so successful in hiding his amusement at the lady's words. If Albert were a betting man he would lay blunt down that the duke's interest was piqued.

"I would not care for that, no. I suppose it is why I rarely go to town."

"Do you not?" The lady studied him a moment. "Well, I suppose it is because you're always too busy scribbling in that book of yours."

Albert choked on his drink, looking about to see who had heard Lady Sophie. Penworth narrowed his eyes, and with terribly bad timing, Lady Victoria joined them.

"You are all looking like a jolly fun party over here. What are we discussing?"

"We were discussing why Lord Melvin does not attend town. I merely mentioned the books he's always scribbling in."

"Really?" Victoria said, her tone interested. "And what book is that, Lord Melvin?"

He shrugged, not willing to tell anyone, certainly Penworth and Lady Sophie, what book he was always scribbling in. How on earth Lady Sophie would know to say such a thing was beyond him. Had his staff been talking about him around the village? He did not care for such things, if that was the case, and would put a stop to it immediately.

"Father tells me he often sees you riding out to your

hunting lodge. He has called on you a time or two there, but you've always had your head down at your desk, scribbling away, and so he has not disturbed you. Our property line, you see," Lady Sophie explained to Victoria and Penworth, "is very close to Lord Melvin's hunting lodge. Father often rides the boundaries, and that is when he noticed you, my lord. Please do not think he is stalking you, for he is not." She chuckled, a tinkling laugh that grated on Albert's nerves.

"How interesting." Victoria watched him a moment before she said, "And what makes your father suspect that it is a book that his lordship is scribbling away in?"

Lady Sophie shrugged, her attention shifting to other parts of the room and showing she was losing interest in the conversation. "Oh, he is merely guessing. Was it a book, my lord? Or merely a letter?"

Albert cleared his throat. "A letter. I should be so clever to write a book."

Victoria thought over the words a moment before she said, "Lord Melvin, now that the other guests are busy playing cards, I thought we should have some music and dancing. I will play the pianoforte if you like and Josh may dance with Miss Eberhardt who looks a little lonely over by the fire."

They all turned to look at the miss, only to see her fiddling with the bodice of her gown.

Albert cleared his throat. "Of course. A lively tune, if you please, Lady Victoria."

She dipped into a curtsy, heading over to the pianoforte. He watched as Penworth followed his sister and discussed something before crossing the room and asking Miss Eberhardt to dance. The young woman looked a little star-struck at having been asked to dance by a duke.

They danced for several minutes to a reel, and Albert

found it wasn't so bad to be sociable, take part in the conversation, and listen to people's lives. He so often was stuck in his own little world that it was hard to step away from the lives he created and live in the one gifted to him.

Albert caught sight of Victoria while she played the pianoforte, her straight back, her smile at the dancers as she played. A proficient who did not need to look at the music sheets to know the notes. He hoped she had not listened too much into what Lady Sophie had said about his writing. That side of him was so personal, an element he hadn't shared with anyone. To tell Victoria of his writing persona, his books, he would need to be sure she was the woman to be his wife. No one other than his bride could know. It was part of the secrecy, the mystery of Elbert Retsek, the unknown. To be known, even by one person, was a serious undertaking and not to be taken lightly.

*V*ictoria played a minuet and watched her brother lead Miss Eberhardt about the floor. The young woman looked half in love with her sibling already, and the dance had only just begun. Poor lass, she would not get all that she dreamed of regarding her brother. Her brother's constant glances at Lady Sophie told Victoria he had become a little spellbound by the woman's beauty.

As for Albert, he seemed to be progressing well, certainly conversation between himself and Sophie hadn't stalled, not even when her idiot brother became mute and could not speak for a full five minutes after their initial introductions.

Josh had never acted like such a fool. Maybe he was in love.

She hummed to the music, her mama and the other guests present in the adjoining room playing cards, their laughter,

147

and the murmuring sound of chatter notifying the night a success for Albert.

Pride rose in her at her accomplishment for his lordship. He was capable, and when prodded, willing to do his part as a peer of the realm, entertain and make pretty ladies blush.

Lady Sophie reached up to hold Lord Melvin's shoulder, and Victoria missed a key. She checked her position on the pianoforte and continued, hoping no one noticed her fumble.

The song continued for several more bars, and with each one, just as the music was lively, so too was Lady Sophie's exploits. Was she smiling up at Lord Melvin a little too brightly now? Why was he laughing?

The pit of her stomach twisted. She would not be jealous of Lord Melvin finding another to converse with and company to enjoy. He appreciated her companionship too, and he needed to find a wife. She had told him often enough that she would not marry again.

A little niggling doubt settled in her mind that she was jealous of Albert and Lady Sophie. That seeing them together had sparked discontent in her she hadn't thought would arise.

She didn't want him for herself. She had plans. Countries to visit, her inheritance to spend. A life to live without being made a fool of by a runaway husband. Didn't she?

The song came to an end, and she smiled at the short applause from the guests before making a hasty exit from the room. She swallowed hard, heading for the back of the house and the servant stairs, not wanting to come across any guests. She could not breathe, her corset too tight, her gown restricting.

A hand reached out and spun her about, just as she swiped at her cheeks, horrified that she was upset.

What was she so unsettled about? She was being a silly little ninny who needed to remember all that she wanted in life. It was certainly not the man gazing down at her with so much kindness in his dark-blue orbs that one could get lost in. Quite willingly, in fact.

"Let me go, Albert," she said, hating the whiney voice that had uttered those words.

He reached up, cradling her face with his hands, his thumbs wiping the tears from her cheeks. "What is wrong? You left as if the hounds of hell were nipping at your silk slippers."

"A megrim, that is all. I think I shall retire for the night."

He did not let her go. Victoria fought not to revel in the feel of him coming after her. The care that shone in his eyes and what he made her feel whenever she was around him. Bliss, amusement, safety, all of those things.

"I think we know each other well enough that you know I know when you're lying. Are you still angry with me after our disagreement?"

Victoria had all but forgotten their disagreement, but she nodded anyway, needing to get away. To calm her racing, jealous heart. For that was what she was. A jealous cur ready to scratch out the eyes of the beautiful, wealthy Lady Sophie, who looked more than pleased to be in Albert's arms.

"I am, and I need time to work through my displeasure with you. Please let me go."

He stepped back immediately, and she missed his touch almost as quickly. She closed her eyes, hating that she was a kaleidoscope of mixed emotions and needs.

"Of course," he uttered, his voice heavy with concern.

Victoria looked up and met his eyes, hating the pain she was causing him. He deserved better than her. Better than how she was in his arms when he touched her and made her yearn. To how she was acting now. Cold and aloof. Angry at him for making her feel too much when she's sworn to never feel anything ever again. If one could not feel, one could not be hurt.

She turned about and fled to her room—a coward as well as an ass.

CHAPTER 25

*A*t breakfast the following morning, Albert watched Victoria fuss with her food while eating very little of what was on her plate. Her light-blue muslin gown was pressed so perfectly that not a crease dared mar the fabric. Her hair did not have one curl displaced. The little diamond earbobs on her ears taunted him. To Albert, she was a perfect gem, flawless in every way, noble, wealthy, and educated, and yet, he knew her intimately. She was the woman he wanted to marry, the woman he'd brought pleasure upon. He never wanted her to leave.

Victoria did not look at him. In fact, she did not take part in any of the conversations at breakfast. Merely pushed bits of scrambled egg around her plate. Was she making some face with it?

"I'm sorry for being late, but I must ask that we postpone any invitations or plans for the day. I have a terrible megrim, and I cannot understand as to why," the duchess said, sitting down at the table and requesting tea immediately from a footman.

Albert hid his grin behind his coffee cup, knowing only

too well it may have been the overindulgence of champagne the duchess had imbibed the night before that made her so out of sorts today.

"Mayhap coffee would be better, Mother," the duke said, throwing a knowing smile at Albert before calling for a footman to pour coffee for the duchess.

He cleared his throat. "I do not believe we have anything planned today that cannot be altered, Your Grace."

Albert turned to Victoria, who continued to be uninterested in the conversation going on about her. "Lady Victoria, do you not agree?"

She looked at him then, and he fought the urge to go to her. She looked wretched. Was she, too, ill? Was there an illness in the household that he did not know about? Perhaps the duchess was not suffering the implications from too much wine.

"Pardon?" she asked, looking to her mama for clarification. "What do I agree to?"

The duchess grimaced. "That today, I think we should postpone any invitations or callers. I am not feeling the best, my dear."

"Oh." Her eyes widened, as if only now noticing her mama's paleness. "I will write to Miss Eberhardt immediately after breakfast and ask her to come tomorrow." Victoria placed down her fork, signaling she had finished her meal. "Would you like for me to keep you company today, Mama? I'm more than happy to."

Albert supposed if Victoria were going to be busy with nursing her parent, he would walk out to the hunting lodge and write for the day. He was still several pages behind on where he would like to be, and he had left his heroine in a most awkward predicament that he needed to write her out of.

"That is not necessary, darling. I shall feel better after a tisane and some peace and quiet."

Breakfast was a silent affair after the short conversation. Victoria sipped her tea, lost in her own contemplation. The duke declared he was off to the Camberley, and the duchess finished her tea and some toast before taking herself upstairs.

Albert sat at the table, trying to form the words to ask Victoria what was troubling her. He did not want to push her too quickly and frighten her off. For all he knew, he may have already scared her away after what they had done together. Not to mention their disagreement over her choosing women to throw at his head.

Last evening, she was upset after his dance with Lady Sophie, but Victoria did not want a husband. Was she fighting with her own convictions? Her own hopes and dreams?

"If you'll excuse me," she said, fleeing yet again from his presence. He stared at the empty door she had all but ran through and frowned, slumping back in his chair.

What on earth was he to do?

Albert pushed back his chair. He called for his cap and cane and started for the hunting lodge. His mind was a chaos of ideas and thoughts of fixing what was so obviously broken between them.

But then, maybe she did not want to fix the rift. Was this her way of leaving him, letting him move forward in life without her by his side? Without her guidance in his so-called quest to find a wife.

He whacked a flower on the field, sending the yellow bud flying across the ground. He didn't want any other woman but her. This whole wife charade had gone on long enough. He needed to tell her the truth of how he felt about her. That he wanted her and no one else, let her decide his fate as only she could.

She would either fall into his arms or leave him.

He ran a hand through his hair, at a loss, his stomach in knots. Damn, he hoped it was the former. He wasn't sure he could live if it were the latter.

*V*ictoria stayed in her room for as long as she could before the four walls and furniture, no matter how prettily decorated, started to grate on her nerves. She rang the bell for her maid and ordered the horse Lord Melvin had allocated to her for their stay to be saddled for a ride.

Her fear was unfounded. For days she had been worried she cared for Albert more than she should. That she wanted him for herself, but she did not. There was too much in her future to look forward to, to be worrying about how her friend made her feel when in his arms.

He gave her pleasure. They had given each other pleasure, that was all. To be worried about satisfaction equating to deeper emotions was a silly thing to do. Women had lovers all the time in London. She knew of several widows who enjoyed the company of men after their husbands had died. No one was declaring themselves so in love that they wanted to marry again.

She could be like those women. Not in the sense that she would take many lovers, but that she would enjoy being with Lord Melvin while he remained unmarried.

Her maid entered the room just as she was picking up her whip, notifying her that her horse was saddled and waiting at the stables.

Victoria made her way out to the stables, dismissing the

need for a groom. She cantered out of the yard, into the surrounding forest, and directly toward the hunting lodge.

Somehow she knew Albert would be there, scribbling away as Lady Sophie had said. Somewhere in that building, he hid his author persona, his manuscripts. If there were any deeper feelings between them, Albert would have disclosed that little secret. It had not been declared, and it only added another layer of fortification that she had been wrong to worry Lord Melvin felt more for her than she wanted him to.

That she felt more for him than she ought. Her jealousy had been because she did not want to share him at present. Not with anyone, not when he could give her so much satisfaction while she was a guest here.

But that was unfair to him and the lady who would eventually become his wife. She needed to be more immune to seeing him with others. After Albert married another, she would survive. Move forward and be happy in her life.

"I will," she yelled aloud.

Victoria slowed her mount as she came close to the lodge. Smoke billowed out of the chimney, and she knew Albert was there. Wanting to see for herself if he were scribbling away in a book, she tied her horse to a tree a little away from the lodge and walked the rest of the distance.

Feeling like a thief in the night, she tiptoed up to the cottage, not wanting to make a sound. Albert did not come to the door, and she hoped that meant that he had not heard her. As slowly as she could, she peeked through the glass window and watched him for several minutes.

He was bent over his desk before the fire, his shirtsleeves rolled up, exposing his muscled forearms. His hand was indeed scribbling with a speed that told her he was far away in another world and telling of the tales there.

Her heart did a little flip that her Albert Kester, Marquess Melvin, had to be Elbert Retsek. Not that it mattered if he were not. But the page that she found and now this sneaking away at all times of the day and night to write seemed too much of a coincidence.

She bit her lip, wondering how she was going to bring up that conversation. She was a forthright person. Her best approach was probably direct and without delay.

He sat back, stretching, and she jumped back out of sight. She warred with herself to go inside, to break his concentration when he seemed so involved with his words.

But then she needed to speak to him, away from her mama and brother. Tell him that she had let him down last evening and that her slip in concentration would not happen again. That she would no longer throw women at his head unless he wanted an introduction. She was his friend and would be a help, not a hindrance, until the day she watched him marry.

Only, she could not make herself knock on the door. Instead, she stared at it for several minutes before slipping away. She would speak to him after the dance in Camberley. There was little point in doing it now when Albert was so close to moving forward with his life and without her in it to complicate matters further. Plus, he was busy with his work. All excuses she was willing to use if it meant postponing the inevitable.

CHAPTER 26

A few days later, the country dance at the local village was in full swing when their carriage rolled to a stop outside the hall's front door. Several other carriages lined the street. Other gentry of the area waiting for their turn to come to a stop before the double doors to the hall so they may disembark.

Her mama's attention was fixed outside the carriage window, watching the guests who strolled along the cobbled streets, mentioning the gowns and jewels, who had partners, and who walked with older chaperones. That several young ladies were wearing dresses from last year's belle assemble, which seemed to shock her mama so much so that she mentioned it several more times before it was their turn to alight.

"I'm sure if the young ladies had the opportunity, Mama, they would have ensured their dresses were up to London standard," Victoria drawled, one of the many things that vexed her when it came to the *beau monde*. How very vocal they were when one was so unfortunate to wear a dress from the previous season. "Do not forget we're in Hampshire. I'm sure they try to keep up with the latest fashions as best they can."

Albert, who was sitting beside Josh, grinned at her across the carriage. On the other hand, Josh looked less than pleased to have to wait their turn to exit.

"What is taking so long, do you think? Mayhap the hall is full, and they're turning people away."

"Unlikely," Albert said, adjusting his cravat and checking his hair. "The hall is one of the largest in the country."

Was the man nervous? It was his first time out in society since her lessons had commenced. And although they had covered several situations that his lordship may come across during courtship, mostly they had been unable to keep from slipping into each other's arms. A most peculiar situation that Victoria needed to handle with care.

She liked Lord Melvin very much, and to hurt him with her choice of future, one that did not involve a second husband, was the last thing she wished to do.

"I'm sure we shall arrive soon, and then we may meet the local populace, dance until our feet are bruised, and drink until we're merry."

"You shall do only two of those things, Victoria," her mother chided. "To drink until one is merry is not a pastime that you are ever to take part in."

Victoria chuckled just as the carriage lurched forward several yards, and it was their turn to roll to a stop before the doors. "How wonderful. We're here," she declared, not bothering to answer her mama, who sometimes thought all her children, even the married ones, not yet old enough to know their boundaries.

Two young men ran to the carriage door, one opening the door while the other quickly lay down the steps. She supposed the ducal crest on the side of the carriage pulled not just their attention but several guests who mingled outside.

The music, lively, the hall full of laughter and conversation, floated out onto the street. Victoria stepped down from the vehicle and adjusted her gown as she waited for her mama. Albert and Josh stood nearby, both of them watching the guests outside scrutinize their every move.

"Come, Mama," Victoria said, taking her arm and walking up the short path to the doors. Albert nodded and spoke to several people, introducing them to the duke and his family before they stepped inside the hall.

It was a large building indeed. Albert was not wrong about that. An orchestra sat on an upstairs balcony, gifting the room with music without taking up the ballroom floor space. The room was a mixture of people of all social statuses. A servant announced them to the room, and several families started toward them, one being Miss Eberhardt. Unfortunately, the one woman whom Josh seemed almost desperate to meet again, Lady Sophie, was nowhere to be seen.

The introductions, the conversation took several minutes. Still, it felt like hours by the time they had located themselves halfway into the room, watching the dancers be carefree on the floor, enjoying their night of revelry.

"You see, Lord Melvin, it is not so very bad to be sociable. You are enjoying yourself, are you not?"

He stood beside her, clapping his hands in time with the music. "I find it most charming, and even more so since I have you by my side," he teased. "Will you dance a set with me?"

Victoria smiled, seeing no harm in one set. She took his hand, not caring how forward the action may appear. Albert was her friend, and she would hold his hand if she so wished. "I would love to dance. I did not think you would ask me."

Without warning, he dragged her into the throng of revelers to take part. They laughed, twirled, twisted, danced, and waltzed through several sets. The room was cloudy with smoke, sweat, and a multitude of perfumes.

Victoria was pleased she had worn a gown of less-conspicuous means. Had she worn one of her gowns from the season just past, they would have looked untouchable and unapproachable. As it were, several guests did not come up to speak to them, even to wish them well, but certainly, the local gentry seemed delighted that they were not so high in the instep that they would forgo such an event.

This was good for Albert too. He needed to learn how to interact with others, even after she returned home to Dunsleigh. "You must ask several young ladies to dance tonight. I insist, or I shall think that all my lessons were in vain."

He shook his head, looking less than pleased to be asked to do such a thing. "What would you say if I said I only wished to dance with you, my lady? Would you deny me?"

She could no sooner deny him than she could deny herself a sweetmeat—her favorite dessert. "No, I shall not deny you, but please, Albert. Do this for yourself if not for me. You must practice. And the people here care for you. You will not be denied a willing dance partner. I'm sure of it."

He spun her into a turn during a minuet, coming to stand at her back. His breath whispered against her ear, and she fought not to lean back in his arms, revel in his closeness.

"Whom should I choose that would please, my lady? If you so wish, I shall dance with whomever you like."

Victoria glanced about the room as best as she could. Several young ladies were watching them, and she could see the admiration, the small amount of jealousy in their gazes at the marquess, their local lord dancing with a woman who was not one of them.

"What about Miss Thompson, whom I was introduced to earlier this evening? She seemed lovely and not at all unfriendly to anyone, not even those who are less fortunate than the heiress." The young woman's father had made a fortune in coal, and as dirty as such an industry was, money still rose just as well in society as a title.

"I shall ask her to dance next if it pleases you. Now, will you please enjoy what is left of our time? Or will I need to ask you for a second set this evening?"

To dance with Lord Melvin was an honor, but she knew she could not monopolize his time. He was here for one reason and one reason only. To meet suitable, eligible young ladies to fill the role of Marchioness Melvin. The notion left a sour taste in her mouth, but at the end of the dance, she fixed a smile on her lips and watched as Lord Melvin led Miss Thompson out onto the floor for a waltz.

She was a tall woman, similar in height to Victoria. But where she was fair-haired, Miss Thomson was as dark as night. Her long, dark eyelashes fanned out over bright, almond-shaped eyes.

The woman was striking, and Lord Melvin seemed to be engaging her in lively conversation that they were both enjoying.

"Are you going to let him waltz off into the sunset with another young woman? Are you not the least bit envious, sister?" Josh prodded her, watching his friend as well. "I thought when you fled from the pianoforte the other evening that you disliked seeing Lord Melvin in the arms of another."

Victoria sighed, schooling her features to one of pride instead of the unease she felt bubbling up in her soul. "Lord Melvin wishes to marry, and I do not. It would be wrong of me to keep him from his desires when we are only friends."

"Friends, you say?" her brother said, rubbing his chin in

thought. "The man is in love with you, and you're only friends?"

The word love twirled around in her mind. Lord Melvin was not in love with her. Lust, yes. But love. No. They did not feel such things. It was impossible. He knew that she was his friend, helping him. He would not be so foolish to allow himself to fall in love with her. Josh was addled and nothing more.

"Do not be absurd. Lord Melvin is, right as we speak, putting into practice all that I taught him. Why would you suggest such a thing about your friend? That is unkind."

"It is more unkind, sister, to steer a man toward affection and rip it away as if it is not returned. When everyone who sees you together knows that it is."

"I adore Lord Melvin. He is my friend."

Her brother shook his head. "You are now dishonest with yourself, which is even worse than being false with Melvin. You had better not learn your mind too late, Victoria, and come to regret your stubborn designs on life. Do so, and you may rue that choice and never recover from it."

"What are you saying?" she demanded, although a small part of her knew what Josh was alluding to. That she was so fixed on her course that she may miss the greatest opportunity gifted her.

Josh stared down at her with a patient smile. "I know you wish to remain alone. I do not blame you to protect yourself after Armstrong. Your desires to travel the world, remain a widow protect you from life. But think about that life for one moment, many years from now, when you're elderly, your family have all married and are busy with their own families. What will you have then? I fear that you will be lonely. I do not want you to be unhappy in your older years."

"I will not be unhappy. I shall have all of your children to keep me company and those of our sisters." Victoria loved her brother for his kindness, his concerns, but they were unfounded. No matter what her future held, one thing she was certain of, and that was her decision never to have children. It just wasn't in the cards for her, wasn't something she desired. She hoped her family would accept this fact and move on from pressuring her.

"You will not have family around you all the time, Victoria. Do please think rationally over this."

Victoria fought not to glare at her sibling. She glanced back to the dance floor only to see Albert leaning down as Miss Thompson whispered something in his ear. She narrowed her eyes. Was the lady truly interested in Albert? She supposed she would be. Anyone would be. It should not surprise her that just as men chased women about town, that ladies would show their interest as well.

She took a calming breath, stemming the emotions that roiled inside of her at seeing him so close to another. It was a reaction she needed to heed and squash.

She did not like feeling left out, and, with her brother chastising her on her wants for the future, the enjoyment of the evening diminished somewhat.

"If you'll excuse me. I think Mama is gesturing for me to attend her." Victoria moved away, not looking to where she was going, only that she knew she needed air. She spied her mother and ensured she went in the opposite direction. If Josh saw her maneuver, she did not heed.

The front doors to the hall beckoned, and without looking back, she left, strolling around the side of the building. Outside, the moonlit night bathed the surrounding park and grass in dappled light. There were several groups of people mingling outside, taking the air. Victoria spied a seat a little along the wall, just where the shadow of an elm tree blocked out the moonlight.

She sat, gazing out into the park beyond, thinking over her brother's words, thinking of Albert.

Tonight was supposed to be so easy. She was to help him toward marriage, yet thinking of him with another left her at sixes and sevens. She did not like seeing Miss Thompson in his arms, happy and too familiar after such a short introduction.

"Victoria?"

She jumped at the sound of her name before liquid warmth flowed through her at the sight of Albert standing only a few feet from her. He was so tall and broad, and devishly handsome. She inwardly sighed, hating that she would hurt him. Mayhap not tonight, but soon.

"I saw you hasten outside, and I thought something may have upset you."

He came and sat beside her, laying her shawl over her shoulders that he'd been kind enough to claim for her.

"I am well. My brother is insistent I do my duty for a second time and marry. He even went as far as to say that you're in love with me and that I should consider you for a husband. If you can believe that," she said, hoping he would dissuade her of the thought. He barked out a laugh, but even to her it sounded as hollow as her own words.

*A*lbert thought furiously on how to answer Victoria. What to say to a woman who had declared what he was feeling. He wanted her as his wife, loved her most ardently, and nothing, no matter how many ladies waltzed in his arms, would change that.

Even while dancing with Miss Thompson, he knew Victoria's whereabouts, who she was speaking to, and when she had left. "Your family is seeing a possibility of us because we're spending so much time together, that is all. I suppose they know me, and it's only normal that they would think we suit," he said, keeping to their original plan for lessons on how to court a woman when one was as awkward as he was around the opposite sex.

He'd done very well this evening. His conversations with Miss Thompson were distinguished, and he'd not made a fool of himself once. "You would be pleased with me had you been dancing alone with Miss Thompson and me. I asked her about her likes and dislikes, her favorite flower, and dance. What her ancestral home is like and if she is attending London next Season. And I did it all without choking on my words out of fear of her reply."

"And did she reply to you?" Victoria asked him, meeting his gaze.

He reached out, smoothing the small worry line between her brows. "She did. In fact, she was more than forward with her responses."

"Do you think you would like to court her in town next year?" she asked, biting her lip.

Albert checked to see the location of the other guests and delightfully found this side of the hall now deserted. He leaned down, closing the space between them, and kissed her, stopping her from biting the sweet, plump lip of hers.

She melted against him, reaching up to run her hands into his hair. He loved the feel of her taking what she wanted, holding him close so she could kiss him back with as much fire as his own had been.

The kiss turned in an instant, demanding and hot. His tongue tangled with hers, their bodies thrust against each other, seeking contact and fulfilling a need that burned as hot as the sun. She tasted of champagne, a heady flavor intoxicating his mind. "Victoria, we should stop. We'll be caught," he said, taking her lips yet again, wanting to snatch her up and sit her on his lap.

Damn, he wanted to do a lot more than that to her. He wanted her in his bed now and forever.

"Do you think that Miss Thompson would kiss you so? Or that Lady Sophie would satisfy you as I do?"

"No, I do not. Nor do I think about them in such a way," he admitted, even though he knew he should not. He could not allow Victoria to believe that he, too, just like her brother, wished for them to be more than friends. For now, they needed to retain the teacher-student relationship they had settled into, if only to give him time to win her.

"You make me question my decisions, Albert. I do not know what I shall do when you're looking at me the way you are now."

He stared down at her. To him, Victoria was the most beautiful woman he had ever met in his life. He had based several characters on her and had wanted her with such fierce desire that sometimes sleep eluded him.

"I do not mean to make your life challenging. I know what you wish for in your future, and we have an agreement for lessons on etiquette and courtship. I should like to continue those. Come," he said, pulling her to stand. "Come inside and dance with me. There is to be a second waltz soon. I do not wish to dance with anyone else but you."

She grinned, allowing him to pull her up. She placed her hand atop his, and they started back indoors.

"I would like to dance with you too," he heard her say, and hope seized his soul.

Perchance there was a possibility for them if he stepped carefully about Victoria. The risk was certainly worth taking.

lbert swept Victoria into the waltz, moving effortlessly around the throng of dancers partaking in the dance. She stared up at him, his sweet, handsome face lovely to gaze upon and admire.

An overwhelming deluge of emotions washed over her with how much she adored him. His friendship and honesty, his sweet, understanding nature. He made her question her dreams. If only he had courted her before Armstrong. The sting of that man's deception would never have happened. Perhaps then she would not be so wary of the marriage state. Or the fact that no matter how much you thought you knew someone, it could all be a mask—a lie.

Something told her, however, that marriage to Albert would be different, for he was different. But how could she be true to herself, give up what she longed for just because the man guiding her about the room made her want other things too?

She closed her eyes a moment, forcing her thoughts to clear. She would not debate her life right now, this instant. Instead, she would throw herself into the Camberley dance, this waltz, and enjoy herself until the sun broke on the horizon.

Albert pulled her close for a spin, his hand grazing the small of her back. His thumb brushed her spine, and she shivered, savoring his touch. The man had an uncanny ability to draw her in—a dangerous gift for a woman such as herself, set on her way and refusing to detour.

"Will you meet me later tonight? We could go over what you thought of my conduct here at the dance this evening. Guide me on what you think I could improve on if you like."

She grinned up at him, looking forward to when they would return home so she may be alone with him. Do what she so desperately wanted to do with him right now. Kiss him, tease him, learn new things with him from the sketchbook.

"I think you're doing very well already, my lord. You could, I suppose, hold me a little closer."

His gaze burned into hers, and heat licked up her spine. "Like this," he asked, pulling her the tiniest bit nearer to him. Her breasts brushed the lapels of his coat. She sucked in a breath, advancing closer still to tease her body the way she liked.

"Yes, just like that."

A muscle worked in his jaw. Victoria wanted to reach up and clasp his face, kiss him, no matter what scandal broke after the fact.

"Have you been studying the book?" he whispered, leaning down toward her ear. His warm breath tickled her, and she shivered. "Is there anything in particular that has caught your attention you would like to try? That you think my future bride would enjoy?"

There had been one drawing in the sketch that she had looked at and studied for many hours. That of a woman, kissing a man's erect shaft. Smaller illustrations showed the woman taking the man fully into her mouth. The memory of him kissing her between the legs made her ache, and she supposed it would be the same for him. Or at least that is what she assumed.

"There is one thing that looks to be safe to try." And she supposed when he married, he could ask his wife to perform a similar act if she were so inclined.

His lips twisted into a wicked grin. "And what is it?"

Victoria pushed her hips to graze his buckskin breeches. Albert's eyes widened, but he did not say anything, merely stared at her in a way that made her want to leave the dance right now.

She looked about, checking they were as alone as they could be during a waltz. "I want to kiss you. But not on your lips. I want to kiss you here," she admitted, moving against him yet again.

Albert let out a huff of breath intertwined with a groan. "You cannot do that, as much as I would enjoy the lesson."

Victoria shrugged, determined to get her way. She licked her lips, already imagining what he would do when she took him in hand, guided him into her mouth. Would he moan her name, clasp her hair as she had gripped his? When he spent his seed, what would he do? Would it spill into her mouth, or would he make her stop?

"Oh, I'm going to start and finish the lesson, my lord. That is part of the deal, is it not? For us both to learn while we're able to do so."

He spun her in the dance, and she laughed, catching sight of her mother, who looked upon them with a warm but calculating gaze.

"Mama is watching us, and if I can read my mama as well as I believe I can, I do think she believes we're courting."

He raised his brows, setting Victoria a respectable distance from him again. "I suppose we do look comfortable enough in each other's company that people would assume that is the case. But your mama knows you are helping me navigate the marriage mart. I'm sure she's merely pleased we are enjoying ourselves."

"I would be enjoying myself more should we be alone and back at Rosedale."

Albert missed a step in the dance but righted them before being noticed. "Do not say such things, Victoria."

She let her hand slide up his shoulder, her finger tracing the back of his neck. "I want to see you shatter under my kiss, Albert. Just as I shattered under yours."

*A*lbert fought for calm, his body a riot of wants and needs. He wanted to drag her from the dance, out into the carriage, and have her in all the ways imaginable. And more if she agreed.

As it was, he was glad there were several minutes left of the waltz due to his raging cock in his breeches that should anyone look closely enough, would undoubtedly notice.

He wanted to see her plump, supple lips wrapped about his phallus. He wanted to see her work him, suck him hard until he spilled in her mouth. The idea that is what she wanted to do to him left him incapable of calm.

"What if you do not like it?"

She lifted one delicate shoulder, looking up at him under long, dark lashes. She was so pretty it made him ache just being near her. With a need that went beyond the physical, he wanted her to be his, to have her in his bed every night so he could give her pleasure. Watch her shatter under his touch again and again.

"I shall like it. I know I will. And there is no danger in what we are to do. I cannot become *enceinte* by being with you in that way."

No, she could not. But that did not mean that it made her wholly safe. For him, at least, each time they were together, either like this, conversing and alone or giving each other pleasure, his heart became less independent of her.

He was in love with her, had been for years if he were truthful with himself. How was he to watch her leave him when she tired of the lessons and thought him prepared for the world, the London season. A life without her?

He could not continue with the lessons indefinitely. Eventually, she would return home, and he would have lost her.

The dance came to a regretful end, and he led her over to her mama.

"I think I have had enough of the dance, my lord," Victoria remarked, as she joined her mother and brother, who was speaking to Lord Hammilyn just a little ways away.

"I agree, my dear. Shall I motion Josh that we're ready to depart?"

Victoria nodded just as loud shouts and the sound of shattering wood sounded near the back of the hall.

"Quickly, to the carriage," Josh said, ushering them toward the doors. "Two local men have started brawling."

Albert looked to where the commotion occurred and noted several other men had now joined in the fray, and the scene represented a day at Gentleman Jackson more than a country dance. "We must leave," he agreed, helping the duke separate the ladies from the danger.

Albert helped the duke as he searched for the family carriage. Thankfully it was not blocked in, and they were soon on their way back to Rosedale.

"Well, I say. Tonight was going so well too. Several young gentlemen wished to dance with you, Victoria. I suppose we shall have to wait for Lord and Lady Hammilyn's ball for them to ask for your hand."

"Mama, I hope you have not been singing my praises to everyone who should walk by you. You know that I find such interfering unpalatable."

"Really, dear. How else am I to have you find a husband when you do nothing to draw them in? If I need to converse with young men in your stead, sing your praises, then I shall. When you are happily settled, I shall stop."

Albert watched as Victoria rolled her eyes before meeting his gaze across the darkened carriage. He fisted his hands at his sides. The idea of Victoria being courted, of having sweet, hollow words whispered in her ears, left him to want to do physical damage to anyone who dared courtship with her.

She could not want anyone else. Certainly, from what she said, she did not want any man. The urge to reach across, wrench her onto his lap, and start what she had promised him the night would encompass overwhelmed him.

"In any case, I suppose it will not be tonight." The duchess yawned, covering her mouth with the little silk fan that hung on her wrist. "I am to bed when we return home."

"I agree," Victoria said, a mischievous light in her eye. Albert knew she would do no such thing. Expectation thrummed through his veins, and he counted down the time until she was in his arms and his bed.

Later...

$\mathcal{U}$pon returning home, Victoria ordered warm water to her room and bathed quickly. After the dance, the smoke and scents from the night left her in need of a wash. Her maid helped her, brushing her hair and setting it into a long knot that slipped over her shoulder.

Victoria dismissed her maid for the night before getting under the covers of her bed. The house soon quietened, the sound of the last servants going about the halls and rooms, dousing the candles and collecting any dishes that may have been used in the parlor upstairs.

Victoria sneaked out of bed, opening her door to check into the hall, pleased to see it cloaked in darkness, only slithers of moonlight stole in from the bank of windows at either end of the hall.

She checked her brother's door, saw no light coming from under it, and sneaked out of her room, closing her door as quietly as she could before tiptoeing to Albert's suite.

Without knocking, she entered and found herself riveted to the spot. Albert stood before his washbasin, stark naked.

His bottom, toned and a lovely muscular shape stared directly at her.

Victoria remembered to close the door and snipped the lock, wasting no time in going over to him. He bent over the bowl, seemingly unfazed that she was seeing him in his full glory.

And what a glorious sight he was to behold. With husbands such as Albert to come home to after a ball or party, one would have to wonder why one would go out at all.

Or travel abroad as a widow when one could have such a man warming one's bed.

Victoria came up behind him, running her hand over his bottom. Goosebumps rose on his back, and she kissed him there, along his spine, wanting him with a need that scared her.

She should not be here or igniting a rendezvous, but blast her scattered mind, she could not leave. Could not do the right thing by the man before her.

"You are lovely to behold, my lord." Emboldened, she reached around, running her finger around the underside of his shaft. His manhood jutted out, erect and eager. She felt him, teased him and her stomach clenched, wanting him with a madness that would not be sated.

He turned, staring down at her. Her attention snapped to his muscled chest and she ogled it without indiscretion. With every breath, it rose and fell, tightened, and glistened from the little amount of water from his wash.

"You make my heart stop," he cooed, his voice husky. Albert scooped her up in his arms, taking her lips in a kiss that made her forget all her troubles. Her future, the decisions she had to make melted away as he carried her over to the bed, laying her down.

He joined her, and she pushed him to lay on his back, a

question in his blue orbs over what she was doing. "Tonight, my lord, it is my turn to learn what you like. Enjoy you as much as I want." Victoria ran her hand over his chest, her attention feasting on his manhood. A purple-blue vein ran along its length, his shaft thick and long.

Whenever Paul had come to their marriage bed it had been dark and she scarcely viewed his manhood in the six weeks they were married. Certainly, they had never learned each other as privately as she was becoming to know Albert.

He lay his arms beneath his head, watching her, an amused light glinted in his blue orbs. "Do you like what you see, my lady?"

She smiled, biting her lip as she moved down the bed to come face-to-face with his shaft. Victoria touched it softly, marveling at its silky softness. "I love what I see, Albert. I'm going to kiss you there now," she admitted to him.

She heard him suck in a calming breath, but he did not move or try to stop her. The first taste of him, earthy and a little salty was not unpleasant, if anything, she liked the essence. She kissed the tip of his manhood, smiling as it jumped at her touch. With care, she wrapped her lips about the head of his shaft, sucking. "Is this right?" she asked him.

His fingers spiked through her hair. "Yes," he gasped.

Victoria could feel every muscle in Albert's body tighten. A little part of her crowed that she could make him mad with desire.

She took him into her mouth fully then. The feel of him, hard, but velvety was unlike any sensation she'd ever experienced before. He quivered each time she took him farther into her mouth.

"Yes, like that, my darling," he breathed, his voice tremulous.

Victoria watched him as she gave him pleasure, their eyes met, his ablaze with a need that sparked heat at her core.

"I have another idea," he groaned, sitting up and holding her at bay.

She sat back on her haunches, unsure what this idea would be. "Tell me what it is?"

Albert reached for her nightdress, pulling it from her body in one swift movement. She sat on his bed now, as naked as he. The cool night air kissed her skin, and she felt her nipples pucker under his inspection. He traced her pinkened flesh, laying a sweet kiss on each of her breasts.

She sighed, holding him close.

"While you're taking me in your mouth, let me bring you to climax. Let me taste you too but at the same time."

"Is that possible?" Her body hummed at the idea of Albert kissing her cunny while she pleasured him. Moisture flooded her core at the idea of such naughtiness.

"It's in the book. Trust me, it's possible."

She bit her lip, nodding. "I'm willing if you are."

Albert chuckled, pulling her close. "You know I'm more than willing. Now, come."

Victoria shivered, hoping he meant that literally as well as figuratively.

*A*lbert lay back down on the bed and took several calming breaths as Victoria straddled his body, placing her sweet cunny before his face. He'd never partaken in the sexual position, but he had admired the sketching in the book on several occasions.

The thought that Victoria trusted him enough to allow him such liberties with her body left him honored. He clasped her ass, slipping her against his face, and kissed her.

There...

She was hot and wet, her gasp of pleasure as he kissed her weeping flesh making his cock rock hard. Without inhibition she undulated against his tongue, taking her pleasure, her gasps and moans pushing him to the brink.

She sucked his cock with vigor, enjoying herself as much as he. He teased her, flicked her nubbin with unrelentless strokes. She did not shy away, lose herself in her pleasure, but took him deeper into her mouth, rose to his challenge. He clasped her ass, holding her against his face and fucked her as well as she deserved, pushed her toward climax.

She moaned about his cock as he felt the first tremors of her climax thrum through her body. The knowledge spiked his release, and he came, hard and strong, pumping his seed until he was spent.

For a time, they lay as they were, their breathing ragged, their bodies damp with sweat and sex. Victoria rolled to his side and he smiled at her satisfied chuckle.

"Well, I must admit that position may have become one of my favorites, my lord."

He slapped her on the ass, electing a squeal from her. "Albert, not my lord. Not after that." He gestured between them.

"True." She smiled, meeting his gaze. "What other delightful positions are in that book of yours? If they are as good as the one we just tried, I'll be counting down the hours until we're alone again."

He would, too, count the hours. But a little tidbit of despair prickled his soul. He did not want to have to wait for the house to be abed. Have to wait for them to steal away to unoccupied rooms. He wanted to be able to make love to Victoria whenever they wished. He wanted her to be his wife, his to love and cherish forever.

"There are others we can try," he found himself saying. "Meet me here this time tomorrow night, and we'll explore more of what we can do together."

She flipped about on the bed, slumping over his chest.

She kissed him, a slow, intoxicating kiss that left his heart aching. "Tonight was my choice. Tomorrow I shall let you choose what we do."

Marry me then, Albert wanted to ask. Instead, he raised his brow, giving her a mischievous grin. "A dangerous game, Victoria. Are you sure you wish to keep playing?"

"Oh yes, I like this game," she said before kissing him soundly once again, and they lost each other to several more hours of pleasure. And Albert lost a little more of his heart to the woman in his arms.

CHAPTER 29

The following day dawned one of the hottest of the year, even though the summer months were giving way to August's chill. Victoria wore a dress of white muslin and ordered lemonade out on the terrace as she caught up with her sister's correspondence.

She told Alice of her time here, her enjoyment, and the town dance, but she did not tell her sister everything that had taken place within the walls of the Rosedale estate.

Her mama sat across from her, waving her silk fan before her face as she gazed out on the lawn.

"You and Lord Melvin seem to be fast friends. Is there a possibility with you helping him gain his feet in society that you have not fallen at his?"

Her mother's question pulled her from her thoughts, and she glanced up, noting her mother's serious visage.

"Of course not," she lied, knowing that was far from the truth. She had come to not only enjoy Albert's company but longed for it. The idea of leaving, traveling for years about the world without him, left her cold instead of excited.

It was a turn of events that she had not assumed would

happen, and she wasn't entirely happy about her muddled thoughts. All of her conflicting emotions could be laid at her bastard late husband's feet. His cruelty and scandalous lifestyle would be enough to scare anyone for the hills and never wish to marry again. She was no different, even though Albert was nothing like Paul.

"We are friends. Nothing more, Mama."

Her mother let out a little annoyed huff of breath. "Please, my dear. I may be older than you, and my first season may have happened some years ago, but this is not my first foray into a ballroom. I know when two people are more than friends."

Victoria continued to scribble words down to her sister, but as to what she was writing, she could not say. Her mother's words distracted her to no end. "Lord Melvin wishes for a wife. You forget that I do not wish for another husband."

Her mother clicked her tongue in annoyance. "You cannot travel the world on your own, my dear. Even if you are a widow and heiress, a daughter, and sister to a duke. You will get a reputation as being fast and our family will be looked down upon. Is that what you want?"

She sat back in her chair, throwing down her quill. "What do you mean I will gain a reputation? I will do as I want, and no one will stop me. I married the man you all thought fabulous and look how that turned out. He ran off with a maid six weeks into our marriage, and then continued to whore his way about Europe before a husband shot him. No one will censure me for wanting to remain alone, not after Paul."

"I do believe your brother will want you to reconsider your plans."

"Not when he knows how important it is to me," Victoria argued, hating the idea of being told what to do by anyone, even her family. This was her life. Hers to live and enjoy.

What was life if one hated all that it encompassed? "And I can do as I please. I'm not a debutante anymore, Mama. I'm a widow, such as yourself. Please try and remember such facts."

When Paul had run off, after the initial shock had passed, anger replaced any sadness she may have felt. As a man he was free to do as he liked, sleep with numerous women without thought to his wife. She had promised herself that she would never be at another man's beck and call. Never give them the power to hurt her, humiliate her as she had already endured.

The world was large and getting bigger by the day. So much to see other than English countrysides, grand estates, and the London Season. To change her plans simply because she had found pleasure in another man's arms was illogical. No matter how much she cared for Albert, the life he wanted was so different to the one she coveted.

She could not settle again.

"I know Mr. Armstrong caused you pain and embarrassment, but Lord Melvin will not. You have nothing to fear from marrying his lordship."

"Nothing but the fact that I shall be stuck here in Hampshire for the rest of my life. Every year pushing out another child that will keep the family happy, so long as at least one is a male."

"You speak as if you are a broodmare."

"Am I not?" she argued. "Is that not what we're all expected as ladies to be? Women of privilege. Marry men of equal value, tolerate all their vices and mistresses they have in London while pushing out their children, putting our lives at risk each time we do so. I do not want that kind of life. I do not want children or a husband, Mama."

There, she had admitted it. Her mother's face paled, and anyone would think the woman had seen a ghost. Her mother did not speak for a moment, even though her mouth opened and closed several times.

"You cannot mean what you say," she eventually gasped.

Victoria stood, packing the letters she was reading and writing in the little writing box she had brought down from her room. "I do mean every word. You do not need me to have children too. Or to marry again. You have three other daughters already married with children. Josh will be next, and he will do his duty to the family. I do not see why I should have to as well. It is unfair to ask this of me when you know how against it all I am. I cannot trust anyone, Mama with my heart. I will not have it broken for a second time."

"Victoria, darling, it will not," her mother cajoled, but Victoria wasn't hearing it.

She turned about, striding down the terrace stairs and starting for the lake. She mumbled expletives, hating to argue with her mama but also disliking what was expected of her, even after all that had happened with Paul. It was utterly unfair. Determination spiked through her and she huffed out a breath. It was not to be borne, and nor would she bear it. Never again.

*A*lbert heard Victoria coming through the trees before he saw her. Her mumbling to herself, words such as vexing family, stuff and nonsense, expectations just some of the few terms she pitched out into the world at no one in particular.

He sat at the short dock, his feet bare and dangling in the water on this hot day.

She came into view and skidded to stop when she spied him. He waved, smiling at her and her shoulders slumped before she joined him, kicking off her silk slippers and pulling down her stockings without care to dangle her feet too in the water.

"Something the matter?" he asked her, knowing that there was.

She shook her head, staring down at the dark water of the lake. "Nothing that I am not handling." She paused. "I will say that had I never married Paul my troubles would be naught," she teased, throwing him a self-deprecating smile. "What are you doing down here at the lake all on your own?"

He pointed to the tackle and rod behind him. "I was fishing. Your brother was here but wanted to go for a ride before it grew too warm."

Victoria raised her face to the sky, giving him the perfect view of her profile. His heart did a little thump at how much he cared for her. How much he longed for Victoria to care for him in the same way.

Was his dream for them a fantasy? Hell, he hoped it was not so.

"It is sunny today. It is probably why my mama is so vexing. She does not like the heat," she admitted.

Albert did not push her to find out what had happened, and instead, offered an idea to please instead. "Would you like to swim? The water is not chill."

Her eyes widened, and she looked back toward the house.

"No one can see us from here," he offered when she looked to refuse. "And I've told my servants not to disturb me."

A mischievous grin lifted on her supple lips. "Will you help me with my gown?" Victoria turned, giving him her back.

Albert unclipped the tiny buttons at her back, admiring her creamy-soft skin beneath her shift. "You have a very kissable back." He caressed her neck, nuzzling just beneath her ear.

She pushed back against him, reaching up to clasp his hair. "Come, let's swim."

Victoria stood, the gown slipping to her feet before she ran and jumped off the end of the dock, eliciting a squeal as she hit the cold water. Albert wrenched off his waistcoat and pulled his cravat free before throwing his shirt onto the dock with all of their clothes. He left his breeches on and then joined her, jumping in beside her.

She laughed, swimming over to him and wrapping her arms around his neck. For a moment she stared at him, the droplets of water sitting on her long eyelashes. Her green eyes were fierce with the lake surrounding them, and then she kissed him. Albert pulled her legs about his waist, holding on to the dock to keep them afloat.

The kiss was as wild and demanding as the woman in his arms. Untamed and wicked. Love welled up inside of him. She was his life, and he needed Victoria to realize that he was hers. That being married to him did not mean she had to give up her dreams, just let him be part of them. He would compromise if it meant they were to be married.

Until then, he would play this game until she muddled through her thoughts, forgave the past and welcomed the future with open arms.

Victoria needed time, and he was in no rush. He'd wait forever if he needed to.

CHAPTER 30

*T*he days passed by, followed by nights of scandalous awakenings. Victoria could not remember enjoying herself so much before at any house party in all the years she attended them.

But Albert was a very special host and paid particular attention to her. Her wants and desires. He was utterly addicting and wicked, and she savored every moment in his arms.

The carriage rolled to a stop before the estate of Lord and Lady Hammilyn's home. The house wasn't as large as Rosedale and was quarter the size of Dunsleigh. Even so, the earl's property was grand and very pretty with its sandstone walls, glistening windows, and lanterns that lined the oak drive up to the house.

Josh this evening looked particularly dashing, and she wondered if he had set his cap on Lady Sophie and dressed to impress the heiress. She was very beautiful, but cold, Victoria could not help but think. Josh needed a kind and cheerful lady like his character, and Victoria wasn't sure they suited all that well.

Her mama spoke very little. Still a little put out after their disagreement several days ago. She supposed she would have to make peace with her mama, but how to do so when she was determined to live her life as she saw fit?

"We're here," Josh stated, slipping his top hat onto his head. He jumped down first, helping Mama and then Victoria to alight. Albert joined Victoria and took her hand, placing it on his arm as they walked up the short flight of steps into the house.

Several friends from London were guests in the ballroom and after introductions they joined them. For some time, Victoria chatted about fashion, London, who had returned to their estates and what scandals were brewing in town. Thankfully she was no longer the topic of conversation regarding that subject. Albert, by her side, maintained conversation well with people of his social sphere. He had come such a very long way since their first lessons. He would do splendidly next year in town.

She pulled him aside, smiling up at him. "I know you do not want me to introduce any ladies to you, but I see Miss Marigold Scottsdale has arrived with her brother, and no one has joined them. Being one of the highest-ranked gentlemen in the county, maybe you could go speak to them and make them feel more welcome."

"Was not Mr. Scottsdale embroiled in some scandal last year?" Albert asked her, not moving away from her side.

Victoria frowned, thinking over the past season. "I do not believe so, but then I have not circulated in their group of friends. Either way, that they have been invited here, I'm sure whatever you heard is unworthy of concern."

He ran a hand across his jaw, an uncertain look crossing his features. Victoria steeled herself to observe him with Miss Scottsdale. This what he needed to do if he were to move forward with his plan for a wife. This was what he wanted in life. She could not stand in his way simply because she enjoyed his company and the delights they shared when in private.

"Go and speak to them, Albert. I shall be perfectly well here with my friends."

He nodded and reluctantly started toward the two guests. Victoria returned to her group, moving aside somewhat so she could watch Albert's interactions. Relief was evident on Mr. Scottsdale at the marquess's presence, and Victoria could not help but feel sorry for the pair. The *ton*, when anyone stepped out of line, could be so harsh in their criticisms. Maybe Mr. Scottsdale had been in a little trouble and had not been fully forgiven for it yet. She knew all too well how it felt to be a pariah, even though she had been the innocent party of her husband's whoring, the *ton* had not seen it that way.

"Lady Victoria, you are here with Lord Melvin and your brother the duke, of course. It is good of you to join our small society here in Camberley. I know that you are not used to such menial events."

Victoria turned to Lady Sophie, nodding in welcome. "There is nothing menial about Camberley at all. I have enjoyed myself immensely while staying here."

Lady Sophie raised a skeptical brow. "Really? Lord Melvin and his penchant for privacy, a homebody of sorts I did not think would suit your character or your social calendar."

"Lord Melvin has been friends with my brother for some years, and Mama and I had no fixed engagements, so thought to join the duke on visiting his friends after the season." Victoria pinned a smile to her lips. "I did not think you would be interested in my social calendar."

"My father knows of everyone's whereabouts or at least those he chooses to know. My father, you see, has designs on me marrying a lord or a duke. I am yet to make up my mind which one I want."

Victoria narrowed her eyes, a prickly sensation rising along her skin. "You are yet to have your season. Would you choose before you attended London?"

Lady Sophie lifted one delicate shoulder into a shrug. "My father is determined to see me married, and so I shall. If I marry, I do not wish to ever be in reduced circumstances, and so I think I have two options to satisfy both mine and my father's wishes."

"And what is that?" Victoria could not help but ask, even though she knew she would not like the answer.

"Why, I shall choose between Lord Melvin and your brother the duke. Two of the wealthiest men in England. While the duke has been more forthcoming in his interest, Lord Melvin is certainly curious, do you not think? And handsome, which a husband should be if one is so lucky."

Victoria swallowed the ball of fire that lodged in her throat. "Do you care for Lord Melvin?" Not that Victoria should ask such a personal question, but Albert deserved a lady who loved him, adored him in every way. She would never allow Albert to marry a woman who did not care for him, only his money, even if she did not want marriage herself.

"Does not matter if I do not. He would be marrying me for my dowry and to have his children. Love is not a requirement."

"And your thoughts on my brother?"

A small smile played about Lady Sophie's mouth, and Victoria decided she did not like her. The woman was calculating, and next Season, whoever ended up married to the chit would need all the luck in the world to make such a marriage work. She would not be an easy woman to be hitched to.

"I'll be a duchess. There is nothing more to say than that."

Victoria cleared her throat, forcing the words she had to

speak. "You do understand that I am the duke's sister and that Lord Melvin is a family friend. After what you have said, I wonder if you're suitable for either man at all."

"Really?" Lady Sophie laughed. Victoria stared at her, nonplussed and not quite believing the woman found her words so amusing.

"Why are you laughing?"

Lady Sophie waved her hand before her face, the amused farce carrying on too long. "You are amusing, my lady, and I find it surprising you would care that I would see marriage as a binding agreement. You are the one who has sworn off marriage, after living through a disastrous one. I would have thought you would agree with me and urge me to guard my heart against any spouses who have little respect for their wives. Marriage is a contract and without love, one cannot be hurt. If I was unfortunate enough to marry a man such as your late husband, well, if I did not love him, I would not care if he were shot on foreign shores."

Victoria glanced about the room, discombobulated by Lady Sophie's words. Was she right? Is that how society saw her now? Like a woman sworn off men, of marriage as if it were some dirty institution to be pitied and ridiculed for those who chose that path?

To her shame, there was truth to Lady Sophie's words. Marriage was not something she longed to endure a second time. Nor the children that followed the wedding day. But then, when she looked across a ballroom such as the one where she now stood, watching Lord Melvin, the small lines at the corner of his eyes creasing when he smiled and laughed, she could not imagine not seeing his face every day. Of not having a future with him.

"I do not see you as a foe, Lady Sophie. I merely want more for my brother and Lord Melvin than a cold wife unable to love. While I may not be searching for a husband, that does not mean that I do not believe that love is real and can be found between people. My siblings are proof that the emotion can be found and nurtured."

"But you still do not want it."

Not with men such as her late husband had been, she did not. But with men such as Lord Melvin, well, that was a vexing issue she had been debating for weeks. Not that he'd asked her to marry him, even though he had hinted a time or two that he would be willing to travel with her. Give her freedom.

She narrowed her eyes. But would he really? Men were very agreeable during the engagement, and then once the marriage had taken place, they were known to change their character and minds. Paul's true character—a cheating snake —had not taken long to slither out of its hole and strike at anything in a skirt.

Victoria did not think Albert was such a man, but then she had been wrong before. Her life was all such a mess, choices coming at her, decisions she wasn't ready to make. She needed time to think. That was all.

"I wish you well next season, Lady Sophie."

Victoria bid her good evening and went to find her mother, or better yet, a whiskey decanter. She needed a little toddy before continuing this ball. A few minutes later she found herself headed for the library and, thankfully, welcome peace from the bustling room. Once she had steadied her racing heart and stopped imagining everyone was still talking of her in the way Lady Sophie had mentioned all would be well.

CHAPTER 31

$\mathcal{A}$lbert cast his eyes over the guests bustling about the ballroom and could not find Victoria. He stood with her mother, hoping she would return so he may dance with her, but after several minutes and she still did not appear, concern bit at his gut and would not relent.

He left the duchess speaking to a group of matrons, all of them watching their charges like hawks. He moved through the room, taking care not to be pulled into a conversation that he could not remove himself from.

Penworth stood talking near the supper room doors with Lady Sophie, and something about his friend's visage made him wonder if the duke was enjoying the conversation with the young woman as much as he would like.

He moved on, leaving the room and walking past the ladies' retiring room and the men's salon set out for their use during the ball. Victoria did not appear near either of these spaces, and he stood in the hall for several minutes, wondering where she was.

Was she safe? Had she become unwell?

He started back downstairs, striding toward the rear of

the house, and skidded to a stop before the library doors. They stood slightly ajar. Inside he could see Victoria standing beside a sideboard where the whiskey decanter stood, pouring herself a glass.

"Victoria? What are you doing in here?" he asked, coming into the room and closing the door behind him.

She spun about, a little of the liquid spilling onto the floor. "I needed time away from the ball." She sipped her drink. "Oh, and Lady Sophie is not the lady for you. Trust me, should you marry her, your marriage will be as miserable as my first one."

His life would be miserable no matter whom he married if that woman was not the one standing before him.

"I do not want to marry Lady Sophie. Your concerns are moot."

She sighed, going over and slumping against the desk. "Well, thank heavens for that. I suppose now I only have my brother to worry about."

Albert did not think she did in truth. Penworth looked to have formed his own opinion on the lady in the past hour since their arrival. He reached out and took the whiskey glass, downing what was left of the drink.

"Never drink alone," he teased her, stepping against her to reach behind and place the glass on the desk.

His body, close to hers, soared with desire. Without caution, he reached out, placing her onto the desk. Her eyes darkened, a wicked light entering her jade orbs. She did not shy away from his touch but reached for him, settling him between her legs.

"I want you so much," he admitted, kissing her deep and long. Victoria sighed, taking all that he could give her. The demanding kiss stole his breath and wits, and he knew he had to feel her.

Tease her sweet flesh until she shattered in his arms.

He shuffled up her silk ballgown, pooling it at her waist. The soft skin of her thighs making him burn, his cock hard and aching to have her.

"Touch me, Albert," she begged him. "Please, touch me."

He could not deny her. He slipped his hand between her legs, teasing her bud, wanting to make it bloom. She was wet, achingly so. Feeling bold, he teased a finger into her hot core. She clamped about him, making stars flash before his eyes.

He moaned, wishing it was his cock that had taken her instead.

"Oh yes. Touch me, tease me."

His cock ached, and he could feel himself on the brink of orgasm at her breathy pleas. He fucked her with his hand, pushing her toward a climax they would both enjoy. She clutched at his shoulders, her head thrown back, lost to her pleasure. He kissed her sweet neck, reveling in her scent, her breathy sighs, and pleas for more. She rode his hand, taking all that he made her feel before the first tremors of her release drew at his finger.

Her body milked his digit, and he rubbed her nubbin as the last of the tremors wilted from her.

As the haze of pleasure subsided and Victoria came back to the present, he grinned, knowing he would never tire of the sight of her during climax. "That was unusual, but I do believe we've just covered another act within our sketchbook," he declared, helping her to sit up.

She smiled up at him her eyes hazy with the aftermath of pleasure. She adjusted her gown and settled her skirts about her legs. Her cheeks kissed with a rosy hue, she resembled a lady well-pleased. "Hmm, I do believe you are right, my lord."

He stepped back, and she slid off the desk, reaching up to check her hair.

"Would you like the same service performed on you,

Albert? I'm more than willing to touch you here," she suggested, placing her hand on his cock.

He groaned, running a hand through his hair. He wanted her touch. He ached for it almost constantly, but here and now was not the time. As it was, they had risked Victoria's reputation by being here alone.

Should they be caught, she would be forced to marry him, and he did not want their union starting in such a way. He wanted her to willingly marry him or not at all. Of all the times they had been alone, he was surprised that they were not already before a priest.

"Not here. Later," he suggested, taking her hand and walking from the room. Thankfully they did not encounter anyone from the ball, and they returned to Victoria's mama just as supper was announced.

The meal was enjoyable, with fare that would rival the best balls in London. Albert talked and contributed to the conversation, but he could not stop the niggling concern that Victoria would not change her mind.

Was she so determined to cry off marriage, a life with another after her disastrous life with Armstrong that he could never win her heart?

They had been intimate for some time now. Certainly, he cared for her above anyone else in the world. He loved her dearly and wanted her as his wife.

Did she now feel the same? Did she want him for her husband? Or was she as unwavering as she had always been? How he wanted to break the stone tomb she had enclosed around her heart into a million pieces.

"Do not forget to dance a set with Miss Scottsdale, Lord Melvin. She has not been able to keep her attention from turning to you all supper. I think you have won her over already with your charm."

The duchess turned to her daughter before looking for

Miss Scottsdale. "Are you certain that Lord Melvin wants to dance with Miss Scottsdale? You ought to be sure your matchmaking is wanted before pursuing it," she said, a look of apology on her face at her daughter's words.

"Lord Melvin knows that I have nothing but his best interests at heart."

Albert inwardly swore, having the answer to his question delivered without asking the awkward question at all.

How he wished Armstrong was alive so he could pummel the bastard to a pulp. Punish the rake for the hurt he caused Victoria, and the hurt against him should he not be able to win her hand after everything that they shared due to his misbegotten ways.

*V*ictoria heard the words spilling from her mouth, yet she could not wrench them back, no matter how hard she tried. Miss Scottsdale was a sweet young lady, that was true, and she appeared quite taken with Albert. Still, after all that they had done together these past weeks, only half an hour before in the library, how could she request that of Albert?

She was the worst of people. He ought to shove her aside, tell her to cry off, and leave him alone. And yet, he never did.

He was too good for her, not by society standards, but moral ones. She was a vixen, a tease, some may say. Was her mother, right? Would she become scandalous and have a name of ill repute? When had she fallen so low?

Each time she suggested a lady to Albert, she read in his eyes the hurt. The continual disappointment that her words wrought within him. She was hurting him, and she hated that she did.

The remainder of the ball went remarkably well, considering her heart was no longer in the mood for dancing or conversing. All she wished for was to return to Rosedale, or maybe even Dunsleigh.

This game they were playing had gone on long enough, and no one was the winner. She needed to speak to Albert, and in the morning, she would. They could not continue to be together so intimately without consequence. She was not ready to give him her heart. Maybe she never would be. Victoria stood beside Josh, listening as he spoke of Lady Sophie, whom he seemed to be disappointed in for whatever reason, and watched Albert dance with Miss Scottsdale.

For Albert to find a wife, to move forward in his life, she could no longer be around him. He needed to form an attachment with another, and if they could not keep their hands off each other, their physical desires overpowering the rules of etiquette, then she had to go.

She had to leave Hampshire. England if she could manage it.

And sooner rather than later.

CHAPTER 32

*A*lbert had no time to hide the pages he'd been writing when a knock sounded on the door at his hunting lodge the following morning. Victoria poked her head about the wood, a small smile on her supple lips. Although there was a concern, a cloud of worry in her eyes that gave him pause.

He sat there, unable to move and unsure what to do should his hasty filing away of his work cause interest from her. Make her question what he was doing at his lodge all times of the day and night.

Instead, he stood, coming over to her and leading her away from his desk and the words that a keen reader and lover of Elbert Retsek would distinguish.

"Victoria, I did not think you would come here today. I thought you may still be abed after the late night we all endured from the ball."

She cast a curious glance at his desk but did not ask, merely let him lead her over to the settee, the very one he'd given her pleasure on. He pushed the memory from his mind, sensing she did not come here to find release in his arms but some other quest. Was she about to admit to having feelings toward him? He hoped that was the case. He wanted nothing more than to be hers from now and forever. The idea of not having Victoria in his life was unfathomable.

She sat on the many cushions and throw blankets, looking lost and a little unsure of herself.

He sat beside her, silent and waiting.

"I owe you an apology, Albert. I acted atrociously last evening. After what we did in the library, to ask you to dance with Miss Scottsdale was unforgivable. I've been throwing every eligible young lady at your head since we started your lessons. At the same time, I have been getting in the way of your progress by being intimate with you. I hope you're able to forgive my abominable behavior, and you can move forward with your desire for marriage, but with someone of your choosing, not mine."

Albert slumped back in the chair, staring at the ceiling, praying for patience. How had he allowed this charade to carry on for so long? How could she not see it was her that he wanted, not Miss Scottsdale, Miss Eberhardt, or Lady Sophie. None of them.

"Victoria, as much as I enjoy our lessons, God knows they've been enjoyable," he added, throwing her a rue smile. "I have concluded that I do not wish to marry just anyone who suits the role of the marchioness."

"Pardon?" She stared at him, not comprehending his words.

Albert decided enough was enough. They could not continue this game, not when they would either be caught and forced to marry, or she would leave, and he'd be a wreck for the rest of his life, having lost the only woman he ever loved.

"Albert, whatever do you mean?" she asked after his continued silence.

"I've been lying to you, Victoria, and I ought to be horse-whipped for it. In fact, I could understand if you do not want anything further to do with me, but if you do choose that course, know that it would be unbearable pain for me to endure."

She shook her head. A curl slipped loose and bounced about her shoulder. He reached over, placing it behind her ear, a diamond earing glistering in the morning sun.

"I have allowed your lessons to continue because they enabled me to be near you. I have wanted you for as long as I can remember."

"Why did you never say? Why did you not try to court me when Mr. Armstrong made his suit known?" she asked, a haunted look entering her eyes.

"Because you were Penworth's sister, and I knew that I could only court you if I were ready for marriage. I wasn't at that time. Other things were occupying my mind." His writing, his publishing contracts that she still was unaware of, the death of his father. "But I am ready now. When you suggested to help me, all I wanted was to take you up on your offer. I thought I could seduce you into marrying me. That by being with me, you would change your mind on marriage, grow in affection for me and marry me after all."

Her mouth opened and closed several times, but her continual silence echoed like a death knell. Blast it. She was still, after all they had done, against marriage.

Surely not!

"Oh, Albert, I do not know what to say other than what I have always stated from the first. I do not wish to marry again." She reached out, taking his hand when he flinched at her words. "While I do like you so very much, and being with you makes me feel wonderful, I have plans and dreams. A second marriage, a husband and children would stop all of those from coming true."

While he did not want to ruin her dreams, could there be room for him in them? "We could travel together, see the world for as long as you wish, so long as we called into England every few months. Is that too much to ask?"

She nodded, casting her eyes down on the floor covered with an abundance of Aubussons rugs to keep the chill out of the flagstone floor. "It is. To travel with you sounds so wonderful and free, but children would inevitably come. They always do, and I do not think that is what I want in life." She paused, meeting his gaze and his heart crumbled at her words. The unshed tears in her eyes that told him she meant every word she spoke. "I cannot be the reason you do not gain all that you desire in life. A wife, children of your own. I know that is what you want, but I do not. You hate me, do you not? You think I'm wicked for wanting what I do."

"I do not think you're wicked." He could never think that, but it did not make it easy for him to accept either. Damn Armstrong and his underhanded means, his lack of respect for his bride. "I merely think you're missing out on an opportunity that could turn into one of life's grandest adventures. But I will not force you. I will not disclose to Penworth all that we've done simply to marry you. But know that I do wish for you to be mine. Now and forever."

"Albert," she pleaded, "please do not make this any harder than it already is."

There was nothing harder than losing the woman he loved. "I love you, Victoria. That I will tell you before you leave me."

· · ·

*V*ictoria did not know what to say. Albert was so honest, so open with her, but still, she could not give him what he wanted. It broke her heart that she could not. She was certainly going to hell for being such a wicked woman. "I do not know what to say." Panic assailed her at his disappointment. What could she say? Nothing would help the situation they found themselves. "Our lessons must end, and we must stop what we're doing."

He nodded slowly, taking in her words. "Our lessons do need to come to an end before there is no stopping what happens between us. We have been lucky so far not to be caught, but that luck will only hold for so long."

She met his gaze, the need and longing she read in his eyes crushing her soul. She was a terrible person. Albert was one of the finest gentlemen she knew. One of the best her family had ever known. Any lady would want to marry the marquess, and yet, she could not.

No matter how much pleasure they gave each other, that was not worth giving up all her dreams for, nor his. One day Albert would realize his love was nothing more than infatuation. When the right woman walked into his life, he would know that today she did the right thing by him, as hard as it was at this moment to believe that. He would have his children to bring laughter to the many rooms at Rosedale and he would know Victoria gave him that gift this very day.

"I do not mean to hurt you, Albert, but I cannot marry again. Each time I think that I may wish to consider the state in my future, my throat closes over and my stomach pains me with dread. I lived with a man for six weeks before he ran off with one of my maids. Made me look the biggest fool in England. Society pitied me for months and discussed my husband at balls and parties with scorn, forgetting I was there, listening to their every word. That I could not divorce him, that I was at his mercy, when Paul had none, I knew that never again would I endure such embarrassment."

"I am not Paul, Victoria," he stated, his voice thick with emotion.

She reached out, clasping his hands. "I know that you are nothing like him and it's a credit to you, truly. But I just cannot marry you or anyone."

He shook his head, a muscle working in his jaw. "May I kiss you goodbye?" he asked.

She met his kiss without hesitation. His lips crushed hers, their tongues tangling. Liquid heat pumped through her veins, down into her stomach, to settle between her legs.

She would miss this. This hunger that he made her feel every time they touched. Albert would be the last man she would ever be like this with again in her life, and she would kiss him, take her fill of him until there was nothing but fond, delicious memories of what they had to keep her warm at night.

You're a fool, Victoria, a little voice in her mind taunted.

She pushed it aside, just as Albert wrenched away, standing and striding to his desk and packing numerous papers into a leather satchel.

"You should leave, Victoria. Go now, before we're caught, and you're forced to marry me. I will not have you in that way."

She stood, her legs a little unsteady. His dismissal of her pinched at her heart, but she did as he asked, walking silently to the door.

"I am truly sorry, Albert. I shall ask Mama for us to leave. I will say I have a letter from Alice begging us to return home. Something to do with the baby. Are you in agreement with this plan?"

He nodded, a muscle working in his jaw, and yet he would not look at her. Instead, he remained focused on the papers on his desk, his eyes overly bright and glassy. Horror clutched at her heart that he was upset, more than she'd ever thought possible.

Had she broken his heart?

She took a calming breath, forcing her legs to move out the door and toward her horse. She did not look back.

*V*ictoria found her mama in her room back at the house, still suffering from the megrim from partaking in too much champagne at the ball. Victoria sat beside the bed, shaking her mama's arm a little to wake her.

"Mama, I'm back from my ride and have received a letter from Alice requesting that we return home. Nothing is wrong, but she would like us closer with the baby due now in only a few weeks."

Her mother shuffled up on the numerous cushions at her back, blinking away her sleepiness. "Alice wrote again? I received a letter only yesterday stating all was well."

Victoria shrugged, not liking the fact she was lying to her dearest mama, but knowing it was necessary. "I do not know about the letter you received. I only know of the one that she sent to me that arrived today." She stood, going over to the bell pull. "Should I ring for your maid to have the packing started? I have already instructed mine to ready things for home."

Her mother tossed back the blankets, and Victoria knew they were going home. If there was one thing her mama prided most about her role in life, it was that of mother, and if her child needed her, made up or not, she would return home and cluck over her for weeks.

"Of course, ring the bell, dear. We shall depart today. It is not yet noon, and if we hurry, we should be home just after nightfall."

Victoria rang the bell, only too ready to return home to Dunsleigh.

Oh, who was she kidding? She was not returning to Dunsleigh. She was running away like the coward she was. And not only did she know it, but she was also certain Albert knew it as well.

CHAPTER 33

"Can someone please explain why the carriage is preparing to leave for Dunsleigh? I saw our driver helping with the loading of trunks," Josh asked, walking into her room.

Victoria looked up from her desk in her room where she had been sitting the past half hour, hoping her escape from Rosedale would occur before Lord Melvin returned from his hunting lodge.

It was rude of her to leave without saying a formal good-bye, but the one she had endured with him at the lodge was bad enough. She could not face him again.

"Mama and I are returning to Dunsleigh. Alice has requested that we return home." And she just hoped she was able to talk to her sister before she arrived at Dunsleigh's door and Alice outed her lie for what it was. Her mother would never forgive her that she had made them flee Rosedale when there was no valid reason to do so. Even if Lord Melvin knew of her excuse, her mama could never know the truth of it.

Never know that her daughter had been partaking in

scandalous liaisons with a man, not her husband. And not only that but then to leave without marrying him as he wished.

"This hasn't got anything to do with you and Lord Melvin does it, Victoria? I know that he has been courting you. He asked for my permission to court and propose when the time came. I gave him my blessing, of course. He is a man of honor and good standing. You are not running away, are you?"

How on earth did her brother know her shameful truth?

"I do not wish to marry Lord Melvin, and it is unkind to him to allow him to believe that I do so. While I have been instructing him in the art of finding a wife, working through his nerves when about ladies and crowds, he has somehow seen me as his future bride and not another in the middle of it all. That cannot happen."

Her brother crossed his arms, a pronounced frown between his brows. "And why can it not happen? He's a kind and honorable gentleman. More so than Armstrong ever was or even myself. He's titled and not a gambler or a violent man, a good match for you, whom I love. You ought not to be so quick to dismiss his affections."

Victoria took a calming breath, knowing all of this already and having been warring with herself the whole morning. She thought of her sisters, their happy marriages. Wondering if she'd done the right thing. If she were acting foolish.

"Will you be returning home with us, Josh?" she queried, ignoring his continued defense of his friend. How could she not try to change the subject? She had no defense against her brother's words, for everything he said was true.

Albert was wonderful and she was running away.

"I have ordered the carriage to be returned to the stable. We shall leave tomorrow and not run off like highwaymen in the night." Her brother sighed, coming over to her desk, staring down at her with something akin to pity. "Armstrong did you wrong, sister, but that does not make every gentleman after him ineligible or incapable of standing at the end of an aisle to marry you and mean every word that they say. To honor and love. You are Lady Victoria Worthingham, a duke's daughter and sister to one. Do not let that bastard late husband of yours ruin your future as well as your past. You do not deserve to live alone and without love." He reached out and chucked her under the chin. "Let Melvin love you. I know he will not disappoint you."

Victoria's eyes burned at her brother's words, and she blinked to clear her vision. Swallowing the lump that formed in her throat. "Even if what you say is true, Albert wants children. That is no longer a desire within me. I want to travel. He has an estate in Hampshire that needs to be overseen. We are not compatible even if I wished it so."

"You want this solitary life so strongly, Victoria? Truly, because I fear if we leave tomorrow, Lord Melvin, after all your tutoring of him in the ways of courting a lady, will marry by the end of next season. He is an honorable catch. Are you willing to stand by when you return from your travels to see him settled and happy?"

The idea of seeing Albert so made her catch her breath, but this was for the best.

"I am willing to let him go and marry another," she heard herself say. And while her mind calmed, her heart was another matter entirely. It twisted to a painful degree, and she cringed, wondering if it would ever untangle itself to beat normally again.

Something told her it never would.

.   .   .

207

*A*lbert returned to Rosedale late that evening, having decided to miss dinner and continue writing. So he was surprised when he walked into the foyer and found his butler waiting for him.

"My lord, the duchess and Lady Victoria are to depart in the morning. Her Grace wanted you informed the moment you returned."

"Of course. Thank you," he said. He had thought they would have gone today after Victoria returned to the house, and guilt pricked that he had not returned as host to dine with his guests.

He supposed he would have to apologize to them when they broke their fast in the morning.

The house was quiet, and he requested his dinner in the library. The fire burned brightly upon entering the room, and he was relieved to see Penworth had not waited up to speak to him. No doubt he would want to know why his clandestine courting of his sister had not worked.

He flopped down on a chair, kicking off his boots and warming them before the fire. The night was chillier than normal, and his stomach rumbled when the butler entered with his tray of roast lamb, vegetables, and his cook's delicious gravy.

He dismissed his staff, sending them to bed at this late hour, and ate his meal. Going over to the decanter of whiskey and pouring himself a hefty glass, he drank it down, deciding instead of pouring another, he'd just take the bottle over to where he was settled and drink as much as he liked.

The alcohol would numb the pain coursing through his heart. He had hoped and thought that with what had happened between himself and Victoria that she would come to feel something for him. More than benign friendship.

That her emotions were not so injured from her previous marriage that she may come to feel something for him.

Were women able to hide their sentiments so very well? He had been schooled that they could not, that they were emotional creatures, likely to fly into a fit of rage or an abundance of tears.

But he no longer thought that way. Victoria was the opposite of such women.

He finished his meal and the sweet vanilla biscuits that were left on a side plate before pouring himself another glass of the amber, dulling liquid.

He lay back on the settee, watching the flames in the grate, sipping his drink. Well, at least he had tried, which was more than he used to do. Victoria had given him that gift at least. He could take what she had taught him, his newfound confidence that he would work on making stronger in the coming months before the London Season next year. He would return to London and try to find a woman who sparked his desire and challenged his mind. A rare gem and one who would not be Lady Victoria Worthingham. For no doubt, she would not even be there.

She would be living her dream life on the continent, seeing and meeting all kinds of people while guarding her heart from feeling anything for anyone ever again.

He poured another glass, the room spinning as he drank it down—until he saw and felt nothing at all.

CHAPTER 34

ictoria was foxed. A disgraceful act and one she was not proud of. Still, nevertheless, she had imbibed too much wine at dinner, followed by proclaiming she was going to bed early, only to then sneak out to the upstairs parlor where she found another bottle of brandy that had been sweet and tempting.

She wandered through the house, no longer caring who came upon her or what her brother and mother would say if they knew she was three sheets to the wind. That Albert had failed to arrive for dinner was her fault. She had made him feel unwanted and alone in his own home. By telling him of her wishes, breaking his heart, he had not been able to face her. She had made him feel a fool, unworthy of her.

Would he ever forgive her?

Albert was sweet, charming, and made her feel things no other man ever had. To throw him aside was not an easy choice. She hated that she had hurt his feelings. In truth, he should never forgive her for her callous actions.

The memory of his touch taunted her. His kisses, his warm body against hers, touching her, making her scream.

His laughter and smile. She shivered, knowing that she would miss him even with all the adventures that lay before her. Adventures she would have alone with only her servants for company. Miles of travel, and no intimate interludes to make the distance shorter. No romantic strolls or dinners on foreign shores.

Alone. Alone. Alone.

She downed more brandy from the bottle, only to find nothing but a dribble left. She held it up to the moonlight coming in through large windows in the foyer and realized she'd drank it all.

Oh dear Lord, she would pay for her trouble tomorrow, and she had a carriage ride to endure.

Victoria stumbled into the library, the only light illuminating the room coming from the fire that burned in the grate. Her heart stopped at the sight of the sole occupant seated alone—a pensive look on his profile.

Albert...

Her stomach did a little flip, a nervous titter that he may not want to see her. That his inability to attend dinner had been purposeful. That he disliked her now more than anyone on the planet.

He ought to. She was a terrible person.

She hoped that was not the case. She liked him very much, even if their wishes for the future differed. They could still be friends.

Would he allow her even to ask?

Victoria shut the door and stumbled over to the settee. Having thought to be alone, Albert jumped at her less-than-accomplished appearance before his visage shuttered like a book.

Closed and read to completion.

"Leave, Victoria. There is nothing more to say between us. And need I remind you, should we be caught alone in a closed-off room, you will be my wife, and no matter how much you want your freedom, that will not happen after the fact."

His words were a little slow compared to how he spoke normally. She slumped down beside him, ignoring his warning, and met his gaze. His eyes were glassy and unfocused. "Are you foxed as well? It seems we both have drowned our sorrows into a bottle this evening."

He shifted away from her, and she hated that he did not want to be close to her. A little voice reminded her this was a good thing. She did not want him for herself.

Even so, the move pierced her pride.

"I do not wish for us to be enemies, Albert." Victoria realized she was still clasping the brandy bottle to her chest. She placed it down on the floor. Albert watched her with quiet calm. More than what she could say for herself. Being near him again, alone and in the middle of the night, left her hungry for his touch.

There was something off about wanting a man for what he could do to her but not want the commitment of the action. Maybe one day, women could live life so, but she could not, and being here, she was risking her future alone.

She ought to leave as he said, but she could not make herself move an inch. "Please do not hate me. I could not bear that," she whispered.

He lay his head on the back of the settee, staring up at the ceiling. His throat moved as he swallowed, and she followed the lines of his jaw, the cutting edge to his handsome face, the stubbled jaw after a day of not shaving. He looked disheveled and handsome. And he was telling her to leave.

"I do not hate you, Victoria, but you do not want me. Do not be caught in here and then be forced into a union you do not want. I could not stand it if you viewed our marriage as bad as your first."

She understood all that he said, but still, she did not move. No one was up. They were perfectly safe. And while she did not want to be his wife, she did not want to be anyone's wife. That did not mean she did not crave his touch. His sweet, intoxicating kisses left her breathless, kisses that would keep her warm at night for the many years to come when she was alone.

That word again...alone.

"We can spend some time together before I leave tomorrow, Albert."

A growl of disapproval tore from him. If he meant to dissuade her, he was mistaken. The sound merely made her crave him more. "Do not say such things. They are unfair."

The despair she heard in his voice wrenched at her heart. She did not want him to be sad and disillusioned with her plight, but she also did not want to leave him alone. But she was unjust. Her actions these past weeks all had been.

Maybe you wish to be his wife and have adventures with him and not strangers in foreign places?

She met his gaze, and time stood still. Her body shivered with need, alive with want of him. His eyes burned with a hunger that ought to scare her away, but it did not. Victoria took a calming breath, steadying herself as much as she could as Albert watched her with a longing she'd never seen before.

"Even after your denial of me, I still want you. I am selfish enough to want to have you, even if I must let you go upon daybreak," he said, a deep gravelly plea. He reached out and traced her jaw with his finger, sliding his thumb over her bottom lip. She kissed his digit before he pulled his hand away, forcing it at his side.

The words, an appeal, called at a part of her no longer willing to adhere to rules. She wanted the man before her but without the constraints of marriage. What was wrong with that?

213

Nothing.

Victoria closed the space between them and kissed Albert. She sighed as their lips touched, meshed into a conflagration of emotions. His raw need matched hers and she clasped his shoulders, working to sit on his lap. His manhood jutted against her core. She undulated against him—teasing them until they were both gasping for breath.

He groaned, one hand gripping her bottom, grinding her against him. The feeling was exquisite, and she wanted more.

Cool air kissed the tops of her legs, and she didn't try to stop Albert when he fumbled with her dress, moving it out of the way. His strong, large hand slid up her leg, flexing against her muscle, tickling her inner thigh. She held her breath as his fingers came achingly close to her sex.

"Touch me," she pleaded, needing him there. Not just his hands, but all of him. "I want you, Albert." And she did want him, in her own strange way. She may not wish to marry, to have children, but she did want him. Who would not? He was everything a woman such as herself hoped for in a husband, a partner in life. He was nothing like Paul.

He grazed the curls at her apex before slipping deeper, teasing her aching flesh. She sucked in a hiss of breath, working herself against his hand. The feeling, too delicious to stop.

Victoria sat back, fumbling with the front falls of his breeches, needing him closer, wanting him inside her.

"Victoria," Albert gasped. He stilled her hand working him, he was harder than she'd ever felt him before. His penis jutted and thrust against her palm even as he tried to pull them back from the brink.

"We do not need to do this. There are risks. If you're so certain that you're not marrying me, you should not do this."

Victoria considered his words. Thoughts that had been racing around in her mind these past minutes. But she could no sooner hold back the sun on a new morning than stop what they were doing. "I want to give this to you. To us both."

His eyes flared at her words, but he reached up, clasping her hair at her nape, pulling her down for a kiss. "Just remember that I offered to stop."

She grinned, lifting herself a little and placing him at her core. "I'll remember everything," she said, coming down on him in one swift movement, taking his virginity. And if Victoria were honest with herself, her heart.

CHAPTER 35

*A*lbert could not catch his breath. He held still, struck a little dumb as Victoria took him into her. He could do nothing but watch her. Her eyes closed, her long lashes fanning over her flushed cheeks. Her plump lips opened on a sigh of satisfaction that went directly to his soul. He shivered, fighting the urge to dominate, to take all that he could after the gift she had bestowed on him.

For so long, he had wanted her in this way, to do everything in the sketchbook they studied. The past weeks, the positions, the pleasure they had wrought on each other had led them here. To trust and give to each other fully. How was he ever to let her walk away now? The idea of years without the woman in his arms, of warming his bed, stretched endlessly and left him panicked.

How was it that she had remained immune to his love? He could not hate Armstrong more for the damage he wrought.

"Are you well?" he managed to ask.

She clasped his jaw and kissed him. "I am more than well." Their tongues entwined, teeth clunked, and all thoughts vanished when she started to move. With the patience he did not have himself, she rose and fell on him, torturous, slow strokes that drove him insane.

Her breathy sighs puffed against his lips through their kiss as she fell into an agonizing rhythm. Demanding more from him with every minute.

"Albert," she panted between kisses, working him with her body. It was too much. Too good, and he wanted more. He wrenched the bodice of her gown down, taking her breast into his mouth as she fucked him. Took her pleasure atop his cock.

Albert moaned, he was close, but he did not want this to end. He clasped her close, flipping her onto her back, and thrusting hard into her sweet body atop the settee.

"Take me." She bit her lip, her eyes hooded with desire, gazed up at him. "Harder," she urged him on. She clasped the end of the lounge, pushing against him as he thrust into her, working him to a fever pitch.

He could not breathe.

She felt too good. So damn tight and willing. A little wanton in his arms. He could not have asked for more the first time he gave himself up to pleasure.

"I need to taste you." She clasped his shoulders, mewling her acquiescence as he kissed his way down her chest, seizing his opportunity to lathe her wet, glistening cunny. She tasted just as he remembered, earthy and sweet. He suckled on her little pleasure bud, fucking her with his tongue. She clasped his hair, undulating against his face, gasping his name over and over.

He pushed her close to her edge, but he did not want the night to end. He never wanted them to cease. Albert sat back, watching as her vision cleared and a question entered her eyes.

"What are you doing?" she queried, a seductive smile on her lips.

"Tell me if you enjoy this, my darling." He ran one finger over her mons, circling the little nubbin he had taunted relentlessly with his tongue. He pushed a finger into her heat, and pleasure flooded her features. Her body swaying to gain more satisfaction from his touch.

"I love that, Albert."

He teased her in that way for several minutes, sometimes dipping his head and lathing her flesh with his tongue. She slipped an arm over her mouth to stop her cries from becoming too loud.

Albert did not care who caught them at this stage. If her family discovered them, she would be his. Selfish as that may be, he wanted her above anything else. Even perhaps her own wishes.

"Albert, I'm going to come," she mewled, working herself against his hand.

He stopped, throwing her a devilish grin when she cursed him to Hades.

"What are you doing? Please, do not stop. Do not tease me so," she begged.

He came over her, kissing her neck, licking the delicate skin beneath her ear, electing a shiver through her. "Do you want to try another position in the book? I have one in mind if you're willing."

Her eyes met his, curious. "Which one?"

In a flash, he wrenched back, flipping her over onto her front. "Lift yourself up on your knees. Hold on to the chair and arch your back."

She did as he asked, no doubt remembering the position he mentioned. "Will this be enjoyable, do you think?"

He slipped her gown up over her ass, taking his time to admire her round bottom, her aching cunny that tempted him. "Oh, I think it will be," he said, coming up over her from behind, guiding himself into her wet heat.

Albert swallowed hard. Hell, this way was good, perhaps better than he expected. Certainly, he was deeper inside of her, and yet she still clasped him tight, milked him toward a climax.

She pushed back against him and took her pleasure as he gained his. He reached around, teasing her cunny, flicking the little bead between her legs, wanting her to shatter in his arms.

He thrusted hard, taking delight in watching his cock go in and out. He squeezed her ass, fighting the urge to spill his seed into her. She moaned into a cushion, his name a chant as they fucked. This was no lovemaking at all. They were taking what they wanted, giving each other what they both needed.

Victoria cried out his name. Her mewls of pleasure muffled in the cushions before her face. Her body convulsed, the muscles about his cock spasming and drawing him ever closer to join her in her release.

But he could not. He took her for as long as he could, pumping hard and continuous, giving her what she wanted, letting her ride out her climax on his cock. At the last minute, he pulled free, spilling his seed onto her back and ass. A messy business, but if Victoria did not want children, something she would need to accept should she ever lay with another again.

For a moment, they stayed as they were, both lost in their ecstasy, before Albert slumped back on the settee, helping Victoria right her dress and sit beside him.

Their breathing ragged, he could only imagine what he looked like. Victoria had lost several pins, her hair cascading about her shoulders. Her cheeks kissed with high color, and her lips swollen from his touch.

He met her gaze, the hunted look in her eyes robbing him of hope. He understood what it meant. A goodbye. A farewell between friends and lovers. Tears pooled in her eyes and he pulled her against him, holding her close. "I shall live in hope that one day your heart will heal, and you will come back to me, Victoria."

He felt her nod against his chest and the small sniffle of her upset. "I shall miss you, too," she said, and then she was gone, walking from the room and out of his life.

He could only hope that it was not for forever.

CHAPTER 36

*T*hey had been home at Dunsleigh for a week when her sister requested Victoria come and see her. Alice had been a little put out that Victoria had lied to return home, but the good sister she was had allowed her ruse to stand. Victoria had her horse saddled and started over to Kester House, trying to build up enough courage to speak to Alice over what had happened between her and Albert.

Since her return to Dunsleigh, her ideas on the future had been troubling and confusing, to say the least. One pertinent reason for her troubles was the vexing fact that she missed Albert terribly so and more than she thought she would.

The other evening while strolling the house late at night after not being able to sleep, she had walked to the library and cried into a tumbler of whiskey—the memories, the fun, and pleasure that she had found in Albert's arms too hard to bear.

If she did not get a hold of herself soon, she would start to think she had a drinking problem.

Lady Victoria Worthingham was no watering pot, so there was something seriously off in her life. She called after

Pickle and Cabbage, her two wolfhounds accompanying her on her ride today. They trotted beside her, eager for their run and a friendly pat from Alice.

Kester House wasn't far from Dunsleigh, and the sight of the estate, nestled in a wooded valley, always brought a smile to her face. It was such a stunning home, and Callum had done a lot to make it perfect for her sister.

She found Alice on the settee in the downstairs parlor reading the latest *la belle assemblée*. "Picking out your gowns for next season already, I see," she teased, coming into the room and bussing her sister on both cheeks.

Alice chuckled, shuffling up a little on her chair. "Oh, I'm so glad you called. I thought that I had punished you enough over your little lie."

Victoria told her dogs to sit, and they slumped before the fire, content now that Alice had patted both their heads. "She is disappointed to have left Rosedale. She has visited here a great deal. I do apologize for that."

Alice waved her concerns away. "It is no mind. She is only here ensuring I am well, and I could use the company. It's terribly boring waiting for a baby to arrive and with you both away, I have missed you."

Victoria smiled, pulling the bellpull for tea, having not thought about the consequences of her excuse she had given their parent. Her only thought at the time had been running away from the trouble she'd caused. She was such a coward.

"I'm sorry for the difficulty. I shall talk to Mama today and tell her you're much improved and merely needed rest. I'm sure that will halt some of the visits." Victoria hoped. Alice loved her family, but being so close to Dunsleigh did sometimes mean they were rarely without them underfoot.

Alice watched her a moment, her eyes narrowing before she said, "Was Lord Melvin who you believed him to be? Is he the famous writer, Elbert Retsek?"

Victoria sat across from Alice and swung her legs up under her gown on her chair, settling into a comfortable position. "I believe so, and I think he writes out at his hunting lodge. He snuck away there often, and when I saw him one day, he was scribbling away like a mad man. I do believe he is a writer, and I do think he's Elbert Retsek, but I never asked, and that is not why I'm home."

"How intriguing," Alice said, a mischievous light entering her eyes.

A footman came into the room and bowed. "Excuse me, my lady, the tea you ordered is ready."

"Thank you," Alice replied. "Bring it in, but we shall pour, and we're not to be disturbed." Alice waited for the footman to depart before she turned her attention back to Victoria. "Did you give him back the page from his book?"

"After what happened between us, I could not bring myself to ask him. I just wanted to flee. It all seemed so confusing, and I've acted atrocious, Alice. I was not thinking clearly or like myself at all."

Alice leaned forward in her chair. "I knew you had run away. I told Callum as much. What happened at Rosedale, Victoria? What did you do?"

What she did not do would be a more appropriate question. Victoria busied herself pouring the tea, taking up time setting out the almond tartlets before she admitted to her actions, her conduct that was reprehensible. She handed a cup to her sister, forcing the words out of her mouth that admitted her guilt. "You know how we have been friends with Lord Melvin for years. Well, due to that confidence, I offered to help him gain a wife by giving him lessons in etiquette, in conversation skills, on how to court a lady while I was a guest in his home."

"You did?" Alice's eyes went wide with surprise. "And how did that go, may I ask?"

Victoria sipped her tea, shaking her head as shame washed through her. "Terribly. Well," she corrected, "not terribly, he did learn and become more confident at balls and country dances. I taught him how to help a lady when she played the pianoforte on a musical night. On how to talk while walking or taking the air in the gardens. But that is not the worst of it."

"What is the worst of it?" Alice demanded, staring at her, leaning forward a little at her words.

"I gave myself to him," she admitted at last. "I do not know how it happened." Although she did know how exactly how it had happened and at her prodding. "I had told him I would not marry him, that I did not want a husband, not after the hell that Paul put me through. I want my freedom, to travel and not have children, as much as I adore all my nieces and nephews. But when I found him in the library on our final night, the pain in his eyes, the longing, well, I could not leave without being with him. I wanted him with such force that even now," she declared, standing and pacing before the fire.

"I want him still. I think of him day and night. Of his kisses, his smile, his silly little ways of making me laugh, and it cannot be. I do not want a husband. I made such an error of judgement with Paul, what if I do so again?" She sat back on the settee, taking her sister's hands. "You must help me. Tell me what I am to do."

Her sister's knowing grin did nothing to help in the slightest. "I will do no such thing, Victoria. The choice must be yours, but I do believe you are in love with him. Have you admitted that to yourself yet?"

"What?" she gasped. "Do not be absurd. Of course I'm not in love with him. In lust, yes. Infatuated, yes. But love? No. You are mistaken."

Alice raised one eyebrow. "Lust? You're a Worthingham. We do not lust after men unless we're in love with them. We marry for life and love only once. If you lust after him, you're emotionally tied to him, more than you ever were with Paul."

"I thought myself in love with Paul. I fear your beliefs about our family and love are unsound."

Alice shook her head. "Paul was not your soul mate." She clasped her hands in her lap. "Why did you leave Rosedale after giving yourself to him? How did his lordship take your leave?"

Victoria closed her eyes, leaning her head back on the chair. The image of Albert standing at his doors as the carriage rolled down the drive. The disappointment on his handsome face. The raw, unmasked pain. "I think I may have broken his heart."

"Hmm," Alice murmured, making her heart beat with renewed panic. "This is what I think you should do before any decisions are made. Our sister Elizabeth and Henry are preparing now to travel south and leave for Paris. They will be back before the next Season starts. I think you should go with them, see a little of the world as you wish. With the absence I think your decision on your future may become clearer than it is now."

Her sister's plan had merit and Elizabeth would never deny her company. Could a little distance and time help her know her own heart? What she truly wanted? "Even if I decided that I wish to marry Albert, what do I do about his desire for children? I have never had those motherly instincts that come so natural to you and our sisters. He will want an heir."

"Have you asked him?" Alice studied her a moment, her eyes narrowing. "You need to know if that is something he will live without to have your love."

To her shame, she had not given him the chance to decide if that was a future he could tolerate. She should have asked him instead of running off like she had. "I have not." She met

Alice's eyes and saw only compassion and understanding there. Thank heavens, for she was not sure she could stomach shame.

"Do you not think you should have? Especially when there could be a chance that you are carrying his child."

Victoria shook her head, knowing at least with that predicament there was no problem at all." No, I started my courses the day we arrived home to Dunsleigh."

Alice breathed a sigh of relief. "Right then, this is what you shall do," she said, reinvigorated. "When Elizabeth arrives in the next few days, you shall go with them to Paris. I'm sure they will not mind. If you take your maid, you may do your own sightseeing to give them privacy, and I'm certain Josh will ensure you have your own private accommodations."

"I do not want to be a bother to them."

Alice waved her concerns away. "La. This is Elizabeth, the nice sister, remember? She will do this for you, but in return, you must do something for yourself."

"What is that?" she asked, unsure if she trusted the calculating light in Alice's eyes.

"That you will return to England and have your mind made up before next Season. I have little doubt Lord Melvin will be in attendance. After the lessons you were determined to help him with, he'll be ready to scuff the boards and choose a bride. But you need to see, really understand the choice you're making if you choose to let him go. If you see Lord Melvin and you feel nothing but friendship, then your choice is easy. It was only lust after all and no harm done."

"And if I do not feel only lust?"

"If you do not, then you need to find a way to win him back. Which if he's the sort of gentleman you believe him to be, honorable and kind, he will be waiting for you to come to your senses."

Hope rose up inside her. She could travel, see a little of Europe, and then decide her fate. Have a taste of freedom after knowing the delights of being in Albert's arms, and then she would choose which one she wanted forever.

She just hoped Albert would be there to enable her the choice. No matter how difficult the outcome would be, she would have to take a risk, especially if he married before she returned and made the decision for her.

CHAPTER 37

The Season, 1810

*A*lbert had not seen or heard from Victoria for several months, not since she had parted from him at Rosedale the morning after their night together.

Even now, after all this time, all he could think about was how to win her love. What he could have done to make her stay. To love him as he loved her. He was certain she cared for him. A woman such as Victoria, a Worthingham, did not give themselves to random people. It was simply not in their nature. Not any of the siblings.

No, Victoria cared for him, more than he believed she could admit to herself. To do so would mean she would have to choose between him and a life she dreamed of living. One where her heart was forever locked away from harm.

He spied her late husband's younger brother, noting the rogue caroused society without his wife on his arm. He narrowed his eyes, the family resemblance both in looks and character ran deep, it would seem.

The butler continued to call out the names of guests as

they arrived. Albert stood to the side of the room, a glass of whiskey in hand, needing to calm his nerves. Although he was unsure if Victoria would attend this evening, he waited, hoping she would. He had missed her, and during the time apart he too had many days and nights to think of what he wanted in life. What he cherished more than anything, what he could live with and without to have the one person whom he loved.

He had done all that Victoria had asked of him after she left. He had attended numerous dances about Hampshire and attended every country house party where his presence had been requested. He went as far as spending Christmas with Lord and Lady Hammilyn. Although the memory of that Christmas party was one, he'd prefer to forget since Miss Eberhardt too had been invited.

She had been unabashedly forward during the week-long stay, rarely leaving his side. Certainly had he wanted to court any other young woman, which he did not, he could not have, for she had not left him alone.

His only escape was when he retired for the night, and even then, she had a habit of walking him to the stairs as if they were courting. He could not return to Rosedale quickly enough.

The names of the Duke of Penworth and his sister, Lady Victoria Worthingham, sounded out across the room, and several gasps and tittering of conversation turned toward the high society family who had arrived.

Albert looked up at the doors, his stomach clenching at the sight of Victoria paying her respect to the hosts. Her genuine smile, her generous laugh hitting him fairly in the chest.

A fist tightened about his heart. How had he allowed the months to pass them by without seeing her? He ought to have chased her across England and the seas to win her love.

To show her she could have all that she dreamed, so long as she allowed him to be part of her adventures as well.

She was as beautiful as he remembered. Her long, flowing locks tied up in a motif of curls, a strand of diamonds delicately threaded throughout her curls. Her long white silk gloves and silver embroidered gown made her look royal, untouchable, and lofty.

She was none of those things, he knew to his core, no matter how she may appear outwardly. When she greeted people as they made their way through the crowd, her smile and warmth were genuine, and he wondered what she thought of her trip to France. Had she enjoyed her time with her sister and husband?

Had she experienced so much freedom that his chances of winning her hand were impossible? He had pinned all his hopes on attending this Season and showing her that he would do anything that she wanted.

He could be the man whom she longed for if only she would give him another chance to prove his worth.

Fear had often clutched at his mind that her trip abroad may have solidified her decision to remain a widow, but damn and blast it, he hoped that was not the case.

He loved her. So very much.

The Duke of Penworth spied him and started his way, leading his sister in his direction, even though she was yet to notice him. When she did, it was like a physical blow to his gut.

She smiled, the little lines at the sides of her eyes crinkling. "Lord Melvin," she said, curtsying. "You do not know how wonderful it is to see you here this evening. I had heard you were in town, but I said I would not believe it until I laid eyes on you myself."

He bowed. "Your Grace, Lady Victoria, I am indeed here.

Your lessons in comporting myself were successful, and I am in town seeking the woman I want to marry."

The duke cleared his throat, biting back a smile. "Melvin, I am glad I shall have at least you for company this evening. The Lettingham ball is never one known for excitement."

"Ah, but you forget." Albert lowered his voice so only Penworth could hear. "Lady Sophie is in attendance."

The duke's attention snapped to the crowd before them. "Is she? Do you know where? I have not seen her since the ball at her estate and I do not mind telling you, I would prefer it to remain that way."

Albert pointed toward the supper room doors. "I believe she is over there," he gestured. "Speaking to Miss Eberhardt." Albert moved a little, so the clingy Miss Eberhardt did not see him again and chase him about this ballroom all night.

The duke cringed. "I think I shall go speak with Lord Clifford. I see he is trying to gain my attention." The duke bowed. "If you'll excuse me a moment."

Albert bowed in return. "Of course," he said, wanting to be alone with Victoria in any case.

Victoria came to stand at his side, and pulled up one of her gloves that had slipped. He watched her, remembering her in his arms. Desire to have her so again licked at his every pore, and he took a calming breath, not wanting to scare her away.

Were they not in a ballroom full of guests, he would wrench her into his arms and kiss her until she realized he was perfect for her and she should marry him.

"I heard you attended Lord and Lady Hammilyn's Christmas house party. How did you find it? Did our lessons help you at all?"

His lips twitched into a bemused smile. "Which ones are you talking about, Lady Victoria?" he asked her without flinching. Two bright-red spots appeared on her cheeks, and he chuckled. "I see you understand my meaning, my lady."

She shushed him, biting back a grin. "Do not say such things, my lord." She thanked a passing footman who handed her a glass of champagne. "You are not supposed to remind a lady of her inappropriate behaviors."

He shrugged, sipping his whiskey. "They were not inappropriate to me. Far from it. In fact," he continued, "the memory of them has kept me company these many months you were away."

Victoria shook her head at his teasing. "But I am home now, and we're back in London. I do hope we can remain friends, Lord Melvin."

Frustration drove through him. Had Victoria made her choice? Was it to shun marriage, keep herself at arm's length to love? "We shall always be friends." The words were thick and all but choked him as he spoke them. He finished his whiskey, downing it in one swallow. "Tell me, how were your travels to France? I heard you left not long after returning from Hampshire."

"I did indeed travel abroad, and it was everything I had hoped. Paris was divine, and Elizabeth and Henry did everything to make my time there enjoyable. When we returned, Alice had birthed a daughter, so it was the perfect ending to a lovely year."

He had finished his book early and had locked himself away at Rosedale during the winter months, plotting his next release and hoping his publishers enjoyed his latest manuscript. He wanted to tell Victoria of his secret, but he did not know where to find the words.

If he thought that she would contact him, write to him, he had been mistaken. Not that he had not thought about writing to her, but then did not want to look as desperate as he was currently feeling.

"Congratulations on becoming an aunt once more. I hope Lady Arundel is well."

"She is very well, thank you." Victoria sidled closer. "I'm sorry that I did not write to you, Albert. I did think of you often and missed you a great deal. I know after all that I said, I should not be saying these things now, but they are the truth."

His gut clenched, and a small spark of hope caught alight. "I wanted to write to you too," he murmured, "but then did not send any of my letters. I did not think you would have time to miss me with all that you were experiencing."

"My sister charged me to travel abroad and to be in London this Season to determine my future."

"Are you certain of what you want?" he couldn't help but ask, even though the possibility of her reply could break him.

"Not anymore."

He turned to face her and stopped at the sight of Victoria's brother-in-law Gerald Armstrong making his drunken way over to them. The gleeful light in the man's eyes raising the hairs on the back of Albert's neck.

"Oh dear," he heard Victoria say, just as Gerald bowed, almost tumbling into them. The cur was due a comeuppance such as the one his late brother never received, and Albert was just in the mood to deliver one.

*V*ictoria looked down her nose at Gerald as best she could, considering the man was several inches higher than she, it was no mean feat. Even so, Albert at her side, a pillar of strength, made her feel safe and above the nuisance of a man she used to call family. After Paul's betrayal, he had mocked her, taunted her that it was her fault his brother had fled to Europe. How she hated the man as much as the one she married.

Albert's dislike of Gerald radiated off of him and she was surprised the man did not flee.

"Mr. Armstrong," she said, giving him her hand. "Where is Bertha this evening? I do not see her with you."

"Gerald, my dear. We are family after all."

"We were family, sir. Not anymore," she returned, her tone bored. "You did not answer my question. Where is your wife? Are you so disillusioned at being married such as your brother that you have locked her away out in the country already?"

The man's cheeks turned a ruddy red, and she was glad of it. He had embarrassed her for months before Paul had been killed in a duel. She owed him no friendship or respect.

"She did not wish to attend the Season. She has little reason to be here."

"Really?" Victoria smirked. "Please pass my regards the next time you see her."

Mr. Armstrong's eyes narrowed. Albert chuckled and covered his laugh with a cough.

"Lord Melvin. I see you are now chasing my sister-in-law's skirts. Are you not an imbecile who cannot speak to a lady without, oh," he said, slapping his forehead, "I forget. You do not speak at all to begin with, to make a fool of your-self more." Gerald let out a bellowing, phony laugh, pulling the attention of other guests their way.

Victoria ground her teeth, not willing for the little weasel to get away with such rudeness.

"Your brother was a fool to let such a rare gem go, and I'm glad to see you here this evening to acknowledge your broth-er's folly to your face," Albert said, leaning close to Mr. Armstrong for only him to hear his last words. "Your pres-ence here is not welcome," he added, his tone deadly.

Gerald looked between them, and Victoria could see his calculating gaze taking in everything he saw. So, like Paul, always wanting to cause trouble and strife. "You will not get too far with this one," Gerald said, gesturing to her. "She's a prickly, cold, miss and a bad lay, so my brother declared. You would have to grow fur, bark, and neigh for her to like you."

The crunch of bone hitting bone sounded before Victoria had any idea of what had occurred. She stared at the vacant location before her that was once occupied by Gerald.

She looked down, seeing him sprawled on the floor, a bloody nose for his troubles. He groaned but did little else. Victoria looked back to Albert, having not expected him to act so heroically.

Having not expected his act to make her pulse race.

"You hit him." She chuckled, covering her mouth with her hand. It was never polite to laugh at someone else's misfortune, but for Gerald, she'd make an exception.

"I would do more than that to him should he dare speak to you again," Albert said, turning to her. "I would slay anyone who mistreats or talks down to you."

Victoria stared at Albert, and the months slipped away, and they were once again alone at Rosedale. His sweetness touched a part of her that no one else ever had, and it was time she admitted to that emotion. For it did have a name. And once spoken, there was no tearing it back.

No ripping her from the man she spoke those words to.

Not ever.

CHAPTER 38

*V*ictoria pulled Albert away from Gerald, who continued to lay about the parquetry ballroom floor, moaning about his bloody nose and his calling to face Lord Melvin at dawn.

"You will not be dueling with Mr. Armstrong, so do not even consider it," she said, leading them away from the kafuffle and out onto the terrace. The outdoor terrace area had not been utilized for the ball, and no lanterns hung from the wisteria growing over the paved space to light the guest's way should they wish to get some air.

Victoria pulled Albert about the side of the house, farther into darkness, needing to be alone with him, wanting him all to herself.

"I think we have gone far enough," he said, pulling her to a stop.

Victoria checked their surroundings, ensuring they were alone. She took a calming breath, hoping that what she had to say would be well-received.

That he would have forgiven her for crushing his wishes

last year at Rosedale. That he wanted her still. "Albert, there is something that I must tell you."

He frowned, a muscle at his temple flexing as he stared at her. "You do not need to say anything. I know that you do not wish to marry again. You enjoyed your travels abroad and wish to continue them as you should. Seeing Gerald tonight reminded me of what a horrendous marriage you must have endured. I will not stand in your way of ever being another man's property."

She shook her head, knowing that he did not understand. Not at all. "No, Albert, you misunderstand me. I do wish to travel, that is true. I loved Paris and want to explore the world further, but that is not all. The entire time I was away, I did nothing but think of you. When boating down the Seine, I wondered what you would think of this and that, Notre Dame, the Lourve, the small, quaint restaurants, and the people. I walked the streets, and the entire time I wanted you beside me. Exploring the world with me."

He frowned down at her, confusion marring his brow. "What are you saying?"

"I'm saying," she said, stepping against him and wrapping her arms around his waist. "I made a mistake when I left Rosedale. I adore you, Albert. I missed you every moment of every day since the time I left Hampshire. I'm saying that although I do not want children, I do want you. I want a life with you, to explore the world with you by my side."

Victoria swallowed her fear. She was asking a lot for a man, for a lord with responsibilities, but she knew she had to be truthful with him. Allow him to make his own decision if a life with her was right for him.

"Would you marry me?" she asked him, holding his gaze and praying that he would say yes. That he would find her enough in the life that they would live and not require everything that normally came with a marriage.

. . .

*A*lbert stared down at Victoria. Her strength, beauty, and vulnerability at asking him to be hers a strength not found in everyone. The words soothed his aching soul, and he wrapped her in his arms, holding her close.

He would never let her go again.

"I missed you, my darling Victoria. When you left, I thought we should see each other at balls and parties, two people who shared so much for a time, but a snippet only. As fleeting as a shooting star. I will marry you and love you until the day that I die." He paused, knowing there was one last thing to admit to her before the night was over. "There is something that I must tell you."

She stared up at him, her eyes bright and full of hope and happiness. "Are you going to tell me that you're the famous author, Elbert Retsek? I know you are already aware how much I love his books."

He chuckled. How lucky he was to have her. "How did you know? No one in England other than my publisher is aware."

"Well," she said, raising one brow, a mischievous tilt to her lips. "You did leave a page of your manuscript at Dunsleigh, which I found. I was certain that it was the same voice and tone as Retsek, but when Mama told me you had used the library to catch up on paperwork during your stay, I wondered if it was you. Lady Sophie and her teasing of you scribbling away at that hunting lodge day and night solidified my suspicions."

"Why did you never ask me?" he queried, curious.

"I knew you would tell me when you were ready. I'm a patient woman. I suppose I've had to be since I'm the youngest female in my family. I would wait forever for you too," she told him, running her hand across his cheek.

"All my heroines are mimicks of you. You are my muse, my reason and inspiration behind my words."

"Really?" Her smile brightened. "How lovely and happy that makes me." Victoria met his gaze, a pensive light entering her eyes. "Please assure me, Albert, that you do not mind that I'm asking for it only ever to be the two of us. I do not think I could survive the guilt should you ever resent me for not wanting children."

He shook his head, more than happy for the rest of their lives to be only them. If that is what Victoria wanted, he would not change her to suit his needs. "I have a cousin, a good man with a good heart who is married and can sire heirs well enough. We do not have to have children if you do not wish to."

"But I have wolfhounds and horses. You will not mind me bringing them to Rosedale?"

He chuckled, kissing her forehead, rocking her in his arms, hope and relief pouring through him like a balm. "No, I do not mind. You may bring whatever pleases you to Rosedale. A cat, birds, rabbits, whatever takes your fancy."

"Albert," she said, slipping her hands up about his neck. She played with the hair at his nape. He had missed having her in his arms, smelling the sweet scent of jasmine whenever she was around. "I'm sorry it took me so very long to understand what I wanted. You must know that had I not been so determined to have my way, I would have recognized what I felt for you months ago. I was scared to trust myself. To trust in what I felt for you after making such a momentous mistake with Paul."

"And what do you feel?" he asked her, hoping to hear the words she had yet to speak.

"That I love you, too. That I want you and no other in the world."

Albert leaned down, taking her lips in a slow dance of

seduction. He'd dreamed for so long to have her beside him, warming his bed. Now she would be there for the rest of their lives. His wife. His heart.

"I love you, Victoria," he replied, holding her close. "I want to have adventures with you. Whatever makes you happy is agreeable to me."

She bit her lip, her eyes overly bright. "How have I come to deserve you? A man who is willing to forgo so much to love my quirks and ideals."

He shrugged, taking her lips in a short, soft embrace. "I've wanted you for so long. If that means to win your heart, I step away from what is expected of myself as well. I am willing to do that. With you as my wife, the sacrifice is no hardship."

"Thank you." She leaned up, kissing him again, and he deepened the embrace, needing her with a hunger starved these many months.

He walked her backward until her back came up against the ivy-clad wall of the house. She murmured acquiescence, and he kissed her deeply. The embrace turned lascivious, and they hurled caution and decency aside, dismissing their location or the ball that was in full swing nearby.

He shucked up her gown, lifting her to straddle his hips. Albert ripped at his front falls, needing to have her.

She helped him, guiding herself onto his cock with an assurance that left him breathless. He took her hard up against the ivy with little care. Victoria clutched at his neck, moving her hips to increase her pleasure.

Her breathless sighs and murmured words of praise pushed him on, continued them along the path to pleasure. It did not take long before the first contractions of her release pulled at his cock.

Albert did not draw out and find his release until she was spent. Soon she would be his, and they would not need to sneak about and grasp interludes such as the one they just had.

"I shall have the first banns called on Sunday, and four weeks from now, you shall be Marchioness Melvin."

He helped her regain her feet, ensuring her dress was back in place to return indoors. "Shall we go and speak to Josh now? He will be pleased I think that I'm to marry his friend."

Albert smiled. "I think the duke shall be pleased too." The sooner Victoria was declared his, the better he would sleep. The anxiety of losing her sometimes too hard to bear over the past months. "Let us go. A champagne toast to celebrate our forthcoming marriage is required before the night is over."

"Albert." She pulled him to a stop as he went to move away. "Thank you for being so modern in thinking. I do not think I could have married a man more suited to me."

He grinned down at her. "I'm an author of gothic romance, my dear. Are you sure you are not modern thinking toward me instead?"

Her smile warmed his soul. "We are a good pair then, are we not?"

Albert wrenched her back into his arms, kissing her soundly. "We are the very best, and I will spend every day for the remainder of our lives proving it to you. You have no fear of ever having your heart broken again. I shall guard it with mine."

"I cannot wait." She laughed as he took her hand and pulled her back toward the ball. An announcement was needed to declare his intent. Lady Victoria Worthingham, sister to the Duke of Penworth, was no longer a coveted widow in town for she had said yes.

The future Marchioness Melvin.

How well that sounded.

EPILOGUE

The Grand Canal, Venice 1817

*V*ictoria leaned out over the balcony on the house Albert had leased for them during the summer months in Venice. She breathed in the salty, fresh air of the Adriatic Sea. Still unable to quite comprehend that this would be her home for the time being or how very beautiful the city was—one of the finest she'd seen during their many years of travel.

She looked up and down the canal, observing tourists and locals alike on gondolas, hanging out their washing or shopping for their night's dinner at local food stalls.

They were to stay here for several weeks before returning to England to review Albert's estates, having traveled from Rome. Another city that she could not wait to return to and explore more.

Victoria let out a contented sigh. How very fortunate she was. Not just in her situation in life, but how blessed she had been to marry Albert. To have found her greatest love within her second marriage.

As promised, he had showered her with love and devotion and never asked for her to change her mind and give him children.

She often worried that she was selfish. Fortunately, Albert's cousin had a male child, and so should the worst happen, the lineage was secure first through Albert's cousin and then his son.

"What are you doing out here, my love?" he said, coming up behind her and wrapping his arms around her waist. He leaned his chin on her shoulder, rocking her slightly.

Victoria clasped his arms to her stomach. "Watching people and remembering how wonderful our time has been abroad. Not just here in Venice, but each year since our marriage. I do not think I tell you often enough how much I adore and love you," she said, glancing over her shoulder at him.

She could feel the smile on his face. "It is no hardship to be married to you, my darling. There are no thanks necessary."

Victoria turned in his arms. They had spent the afternoon in bed, making delicious love. Albert had joined her wearing only his breeches, his toned abdomen tanned and muscular after years of traveling abroad hers to enjoy.

She ran her hand over his chiseled stomach, hers fluttering with desire. "But it is true. I never wish for our charmed life to end."

He kissed her softly, and her breath caught. She loved him more today than the day she had asked him to be her husband. The idea of losing him often made her panicked, so much as she adored him.

"It shall not, my darling. There are many more adventures yet to be had." His eyes darkened, wickedness lighting his blue orbs. "More adventures inside our bedroom," he said, pulling her slowly from the balcony.

Victoria allowed him to persuade her, laughing at his words. "Should we not venture outdoors and see some of this great city?"

He continued walking her toward the bed. "The city has been here for hundreds of years. It can wait another day."

And it did wait, for two days in fact. But the wait was worth it, as were all their adventures together.

Always.

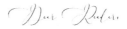

Dear Reader,

I hope you enjoyed, *Only a Marquess Will Do*, book four in my To Marry a Rogue series!

I'm so thrilled you chose my book to read, and if you're able, I would appreciate an honest review of *Only a Marquess Will Do*. As they say, feed an author, leave a review!

If you'd like to continue the series, you can now pre-order book five in my To Marry a Rogue series, *Only a Lady Will Do*. Available this July.

Alternatively, you can keep in contact with me by visiting my website or following me online. You can contact me at www.tamaragill.com or email me at tamaragillauthor@gmail.com.

Tamara Gill

ONLY A LADY WILL DO

TO MARRY A ROGUE, BOOK 5

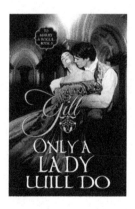

Available July, 2021~ pre-order your copy today!

LORDS OF LONDON SERIES
AVAILABLE NOW!

Dive into these charming historical romances! In this six-book series, Darcy seduces a virginal duke, Cecilia's world collides with a roguish marquess, Katherine strikes a deal with an unlucky earl and Lizzy sets out to conquer a very wicked Viscount. These stories plus more adventures in the Lords of London series! Available now through Amazon or read free with KindleUnlimited.

KISS THE WALLFLOWER SERIES
AVAILABLE NOW!

If the roguish Lords of London are not for you and wall-flowers are more your cup of tea, this is the series for you. My Kiss the Wallflower series, are linked through friendship and family in this four-book series. You can grab a copy on Amazon or read free through KindleUnlimited.

LEAGUE OF UNWEDDABLE GENTLEMEN SERIES AVAILABLE NOW!

Fall into my latest series, where the heroines have to fight for what they want, both regarding their life and love. And where the heroes may be unweddable to begin with, that is until they meet the women who'll change their fate. The League of Unweddable Gentlemen series is available now!

LEAGUE OF UNWEDDABLE GENTLEMEN

Lords of London Series

TO BEDEVIL A DUKE

TO MADDEN A MARQUESS

TO TEMPT AN EARL

TO VEX A VISCOUNT

TO DARE A DUCHESS

TO MARRY A MARCHIONESS

LORDS OF LONDON - BOOKS 1-3 BUNDLE

LORDS OF LONDON - BOOKS 4-6 BUNDLE

To Marry a Rogue Series

ONLY AN EARL WILL DO

ONLY A DUKE WILL DO

ONLY A VISCOUNT WILL DO

ONLY A MARQUESS WILL DO

ONLY A LADY WILL DO

TO MARRY A ROGUE - BOOKS 1-5 BUNDLE

A Time Traveler's Highland Love Series

TO CONQUER A SCOT

TO SAVE A SAVAGE SCOT

TO WIN A HIGHLAND SCOT

HIGHLAND LOVE - BOOKS 1-3 BUNDLE

A Stolen Season Series

A STOLEN SEASON

A STOLEN SEASON: BATH

A STOLEN SEASON: LONDON

Time Travel Romance

DEFIANT SURRENDER

Scandalous London Series
A GENTLEMAN'S PROMISE
A CAPTAIN'S ORDER
A MARRIAGE MADE IN MAYFAIR
SCANDALOUS LONDON - BOOKS 1-3 BUNDLE

High Seas & High Stakes Series
HIS LADY SMUGGLER
HER GENTLEMAN PIRATE
HIGH SEAS & HIGH STAKES - BOOKS 1-2 BUNDLE

Daughters Of The Gods Series
BANISHED-GUARDIAN-FALLEN
DAUGHTERS OF THE GODS - BOOKS 1-3 BUNDLE

Stand Alone Books
TO SIN WITH SCANDAL
OUTLAWS

ABOUT THE AUTHOR

Tamara is an Australian author who grew up in an old mining town in country South Australia, where her love of history was founded. So much so, she made her darling husband travel to the UK for their honeymoon, where she dragged him from one historical monument and castle to another.

A mother of three, her two little gentlemen in the making, a future lady (she hopes) and a part-time job keep her busy in the real world, but whenever she gets a moment's peace she loves to write romance novels in an array of genres, including regency, medieval and time travel.

www.tamaragill.com
tamaragillauthor@gmail.com

Made in the USA
Coppell, TX
23 October 2021